ONE MORE RIVER TO CROSS

ONE MORE RIVER TO CROSS

by

WINALEE GENTRY

Philadelphia
THE WESTMINSTER PRESS

Library of Congress Catalog Card Number: 55-8971

To Dux, of course

ONE MORE RIVER TO CROSS

I

IT WAS ONE OF THOSE DAYS when my fingers felt all thumbs, the telephone rang incessantly, the children quarreled more than usual, and everything seemed to go in slow motion. But now, at last, dinner was ready and I sat waiting for Dux in the kitchen of the small house we'd bought only this year in Eastover Court near the outskirts of Louisville, Kentucky.

I knew Dux would be late. This was the day of the conference, the day the officials of the Louisville Gas Company would finally make up their minds about contracting for gas from the Indiana field and building a pipeline to carry it into the city. My husband, recently made superintendent of the gas transportation department, had built a lot of pipelines, but this one would be different. This one would cross the Ohio — a major river job.

The kitchen felt warm and I pushed back the white ruffled curtains and raised the windows to let in the early November air. Fall was early this year, even for Kentucky, and I thought: Why do utilities always wait until bad weather to lay lines that should have been laid during the summer? You'd think they'd be smarter than that. But Dux didn't seem to mind, and he was excited over the prospect of this new job, more excited than I'd ever seen him in all the six years of our marriage.

And Dux — bless him! — wasn't one to go overboard about ordinary things. I'm the flighty one in this family. Dux came up the hard way, acquiring poise and common sense in the process. He also acquired what is often called an inferiority complex, sometimes a misnomer for that rare brand of humility that makes men great.

Despite his parents' protests, he quit school in his freshman year at high school to take a full-time job. Later, realizing his mistake, he took night courses and finished. Then, deciding that engineering was his forte, he took a job with an oil company and signed up for a civil engineering course by mail. From what his mother told me, I guess he didn't have much fun.

But he had traveled a long way from his first job as rodman to the head of his own department in the Louisville Gas Company. In between, he'd studied geology, made locations for drilling wells, set up rigs, and drilled both good wells and dry holes. He had figured oil and gas reserves in the field, and once he'd even put out a bad gas fire. Everything about oil or gas fascinated him. And now, if only the bigwigs would put through the Indiana deal, Dux's dream would come true. He'd get his first big river job!

I glanced at the kitchen clock. It was ten after six. Covering the pans on the stove, I turned the gas down low and went into the living room. Five-year-old Buddy was pushing a small dump truck along a pattern in a rug, while Lee, aged two and a half, sat cross-legged, bent over her color book, the crayon gripped in her chubby fist. With a gurgling cry, Baby Ginger dropped a sodden graham cracker, pulled herself up by the rail of her playpen, and reached out her arms to me. She tottered for a moment, then sat down heavily on her little fat bottom. I kissed the top of her fuzzy round head and pushed a Teddy bear into her arms.

Buddy was saying, with kindergarten authority, " I told Lee not to put those crayons on your new rug, Mommy, but she won't keep 'em in the box."

Lee tossed her auburn curls and, ignoring her brother's remark, casually bestowed bright yellow ears on a huge pink elephant. I bent down to pick up the scattered crayons just as a car pulled into the driveway.

With cries of " Daddy! " the children got to the door before I did. After their kisses and bear hugs, Dux straightened up and I saw his face. It was grayish white, and his usually mobile lips were set in thin, hard lines.

" What's wrong? " I exclaimed.

" Everything! " He leaned over to kiss me, laid his topcoat down, and, with unwonted vehemence, threw his hat toward a chair. " Everything," he repeated in a voice that told me he was really sunk.

" Come in the kitchen. I'll get you some coffee — then you can tell me," I said, anxious to know what had happened to make him look like that.

He followed me to the kitchen and flung himself down onto the chair by the table. He was silent a moment, then he blurted, " They won't let me lay the line across the damn river! "

I set the cup of coffee on the table in front of him. " You mean they're not going to use the gas from the Indiana field? "

" Oh, they're going to use it all right," he said. " They signed the contract today. But they're getting men from Chicago to do the river crossing — "

" But *why?* " I broke in.

" Addison says I haven't had enough experience in laying river lines." Dux's fist hit the table and the cup

13

jumped, slopping coffee into the saucer.

"Addison's crazy!" I exploded. "I hope you told him so — even if he *is* your boss. You've laid plenty of pipelines under plenty of rivers!"

"No, Shortie, just creeks." He smiled indulgently, then his lips grew tense again.

"Well," I began, "what's the Ohio? Just a little old creek grown up. You could do it!"

"I know I could do it — if they'd just give me a chance." He lighted a cigarette, and it hurt me to watch his shaking hands.

The fragrance of hickory-smoked ham filled the kitchen and, with a feeling of helplessness, I started to take up dinner. "You'll feel better after you eat, honey. Maybe something will happen to change Mr. Addison's mind."

"Not a chance," Dux shook his head. "I almost had the others sold on letting me do it — then Addison put his foot down." He got up, carried the empty cup to the sink, and ran cold water in it. "I guess I've been taking things too much for granted," he said. "I never dreamed they'd take that job away from me."

After dinner I put the children to bed, washed the dishes and left them to drain, then went down to the basement where I knew I'd find Dux. He had always worked off grievances with his tools; the proof was scattered all over the house. He was working now on a tiny drilling rig and I felt thankful it wasn't another boat. We'd had to tear off part of the basement door of a rented house to get the last one out when it was finished. I sat and watched him fasten the little bull wheel onto the post and wondered at his patience. Suddenly he stood up and pushed the tools aside.

"I can't work," he said, moving his stool back. "Let's go to bed and try to get some sleep. Forget the river crossing. Someday I'll show them what I can do."

For hours I lay awake, a million thoughts running in and out of my head. I couldn't for the life of me understand why Mr. Addison, who was the general superintendent of the Gas Company, didn't have more faith in Dux. How could he be so unjust? Dux hadn't failed in anything yet. In fact, there had been plenty of times when he'd accomplished things that others said couldn't be done — like that time last winter when a whole section of gas line washed out in eastern Kentucky. A flash flood had caused a landslide, and the linewalker who called in said it was impossible to fix because they couldn't get any equipment across the swollen creek. Mr. Addison was frantic. With only thirteen hours of gas in storage, it began to look as if the Company's service would fail for the first time.

It was Dux who figured out how the situation could be saved. It was Dux who took ten loaded trucks, tied them together bumper to bumper, then plugged up the oil holes and carburetors of the front trucks so that water wouldn't hurt the engines. It was his idea to have the back trucks push the front ones across the creek — and it worked.

Then he did the same things to the back trucks, so that the front ones could pull the rest across. Dux and his helpers spent the whole night laying a new pipeline around the landslide, and it was finished a full hour before the gas reserve gave out. " Seems there's nothing Dux can't do," Mr. Addison had said at the time. Obviously Mr. Addison had a very short memory.

Dux stirred and mumbled. Finally, I turned over on my stomach, buried my head under the pillow, and drifted off to sleep.

Sometime in the night I wakened and, before I felt the empty space beside me, I knew Dux was not there. Turning on the light, I found my robe and slippers and tiptoed down the stairs. He sat slumped in a chair by the window, the light from a street lamp accentuating the tired lines in his face.

" Want some coffee? " I touched his shoulder and he came out of his absorption slowly.

" Sorry I woke you, Shortie," he said as he followed me into the kitchen and sat down. " I couldn't sleep."

I measured coffee into the percolator, wondering how many times I had done this, how many times I would do it again. In every crisis of our lives — and there have been many — there has always been a steaming cup of fragrant coffee in the background. It has come to be a kind of ritual. Taking cream from the refrigerator, sugar from the cupboard, I put them on the table while Dux brought cups and saucers from the china closet. Soon the familiar aroma filled the kitchen.

" Honey," I began tentatively, " don't you think you could talk to Mr. Addison — maybe get him to change his mind? "

" Talk to him! I talked my fool head off and got nowhere at all." Dux glared at me as if I were to blame. " Spent a full hour trying to convince him. All he said was that I'm too young; it's too big for me; said I could learn from the guy they give the job to — a graduate engineer, no doubt," he added bitterly.

Raging inwardly, I watched him pour thick cream into his cup, absently spoon in too much sugar and stir it around and around. What if Dux *was* still under thirty, I thought. What if he hadn't gone to college? Hadn't he more than made up for it in study and actual experience? Drat Mr. Addison for not recognizing ability when it was right under his nose!

" Lot of good it did to make you head of the department if they won't let you run it! " I flared. " You're smarter than Mr. Addison. He's just older."

He reached over, gave my hand a pat, and his voice softened. "Don't you worry, baby. There'll be other times." But I knew how deeply he was hurt, how much he had counted on doing this job.

"I wouldn't take it, Dux. I'd do something!"

"And what do you think you'd do?" He lighted a cigarette, blew smoke rings above his head, and looked at me. Something rebellious was building up inside me and I said, impulsively,

"Do the job anyhow — when they're not looking!"

"And get fired?" Dux grinned at me.

\"No. Resign before they have a chance to fire you. You can get another job. You're much too good for that old Gas Company, anyway!"

"That's what *you* think, Shortie." He smiled and added, a trifle sourly: "But I'm afraid I'd have trouble convincing the other fellow. Every company has its doubting Thomases, like Addison."

"But, Dux, you might get a job you'd like lots better," I persisted. "You'll never know till you try."

"And what would we use for money in the meantime?" He drained the rest of his coffee and dropped his cigarette butt into the cup, a gesture which I pretended not to see.

"Well, anyway, we wouldn't starve," I pointed out. "There's that country ham Dad sent us, those cases of canned goods we got wholesale — and the payment on the house isn't due for another month. Besides, there's eighty-two dollars and fifty cents in our savings account, and Dr. Speidel won't mind waiting for the last payment on the baby . . ." I stopped for breath. "Oh, Dux, why don't you?"

He leaned over and kissed me on the nose. "You'd be silly enough to hold the flashlight while I robbed a safe, wouldn't you? " he said, a little quirk in the corner of his mouth. Then he shook his head. " No, sweet, I can't gamble with the Company's money."

" But it wouldn't be a gamble. You *said* you could do it," I reminded him, warming up to the idea.

" I *could*." He leaned back and jammed his hands into the pockets of his robe. " I did think of doing just that — jumping out and doing that river job before the Chicago men could get down to look at it." He shook his head again and sighed. " With a wife and children — well, a man just can't take a chance."

" So — we're just millstones around your neck! " I exclaimed, jumping up and turning over my cup, spilling coffee on the table.

" Take it easy, baby." He picked up the cup, reached for the dishcloth, and mopped the table. " You know I didn't mean it that way."

" You did! " I accused him, blinking back the tears.

With a quick gesture, he pulled me down into his lap and his arms closed around me. " I wouldn't be where I am now if it weren't for you and the children, darling. You know that."

When I started to argue the point, he kissed me.

" I couldn't do it anyway without permission from Addison," he said presently. " It would mean renting barges, getting dredging equipment, a crane to dig the riverbanks, and it'll take a week for the pipe and clamps to get in."

He sat lost in thought and I dug my chin into his shoulder, helpless and sharing his sense of frustration. Then he picked up my grocery pad and pencil and I watched the tiny figures fill the page, wondering what they meant. " I'll bet I could do that job cheaper than any outsider," he said thoughtfully. " And it could probably be done in a couple of days." He threw the pencil down.

"Over a week end," I breathed in his ear. "The office is closed on Saturdays."

"Don't tempt me, Shortie." He grinned down at me. "It would almost be worth getting fired to see Addison's face if the job was done when he brought the Chicago bunch down."

He pulled a cigarette from the pack on the table and lighted it, absently. "I don't know how a man can get experience if he's not allowed to do the job. Even if he makes a mistake, it's the only way to learn." He took a few draws on the cigarette, blowing the smoke away from my face, and the kitchen clock ticked out the minutes.

Suddenly, he stood up, nearly spilling me on the floor, and threw the half-smoked cigarette in the sink. "By gosh — I'm going to do it! This is Friday. I'll get everything lined up for next week end." He grabbed me around the waist and shook me, his eyes shining. "You know it's crazy, don't you? But it's the only way I'll get to prove myself — and, by heaven, I'll do it! "

2

DUX SCARCELY TOOK TIME to eat during the following week, what with doing his routine work and quietly getting everything lined up for the river crossing. Mr. Addison had authorized him to lay the three miles of pipeline from the main line down to the river on the Kentucky side, the twelve miles from the Indiana side back to the gas wells, and to stack the pipe for the crossing on the Kentucky side of the riverbank.

By Wednesday night the three miles across the Kentucky fields were complete. Dux told the men to take Thursday off because he wanted them to work on Sunday, which they sometimes did if they were afraid the good weather wouldn't hold. " I'm pretty sure none of them smell a mouse," he said, pointing out that the men just naturally assumed the truckers would move the equipment to the Indiana side on Thursday.

Friday morning we were up early and I was just starting the eggs and bacon when the telephone rang and Dux answered. " That's right," I heard him say. " You tow the barges and the dredge down to the locks and I'll meet you there at ten. . . . Yes . . . that'll give me time to go over things with the boat crew."

I loved the strength and confidence in his voice. He's a fighter, I thought; this job is a challenge to him and he won't be satisfied until he has proved his ability, not only to the Gas Company, but to himself as well.

He came in, sat down at the kitchen table, and poured coffee into our cups from the pot on the table. " That was Captain Wilks. I'm going to ride down the river with him. Jeff Nichols, who's already in the know, should have the pipe unloaded and stacked on the bank by the time we get there." He looked at me and grinned. " I told Jeff to put the men wise as soon as they got down this morning. I'm anxious to see how they take it."

I set the platter of eggs and bacon on the table and started the toaster. " What if Mr. Addison or someone from the office comes down there? "

" Not much chance. It's twelve miles out and hard to find. Anyway, Addison is taking his family to Lexington for the week end. By the time he gets back, I'll have the job buttoned up — I hope." Dux ate a moment, then said: " I'm sure sticking my neck out. If anything goes wrong, there'll be hell to pay."

I looked at the fresh smoothness of his ruddy skin, the laugh lines around his eyes, the quick smile he always had for me, and felt a surge of love.

" You'll do it, honey," I said. " You always do."

He drank the last of his coffee and pushed his chair back. " You all set to feed the men? "

I nodded. " Finished frosting the cake last night."

" I hated to ask you to cook for all those men, but there isn't any place around there to eat. They can't leave the job, once we start. Sure you can manage? " He reached for his jacket and hat on a rack by the door.

" Of course! I've been on food committees at the church. Last week our guild fed forty women at a luncheon," I said, proud of my part in the accomplishment. " Besides, I've been cooking all week. You've just been too busy to notice."

" O.K., I'm depending on you, but this is no tea party. These men work hard and they need lots of good, substantial food."

" And they'll get it," I promised. " The refrigerator is bulging out at the sides. I'll get there around six." I got up from the table and held my face up for his kiss. He put his arms around me and for a moment held me close.

" Say a prayer for me, baby," he whispered.

I watched him go down the back steps to the garage with his head up, his shoulders back, a sort of electric energy in his walk, and I thought of the storybook prince going forth to slay the dragon. It was good to be married to a man like Dux, good to feel cherished, to be able to share a common goal, a common secret —

My leisurely reflections as a cherished wife were rudely interrupted by slam-bangs from upstairs, reminding me that I was also a busy mother. I hurried up to the children and started galloping down the long road of dressing them, feeding them, getting Buddy off to kindergarten, Lee settled with her toys, Ginger in the playpen, and the house set to rights.

After lunch I put the youngsters down for naps and started to pack the food into the grocery boxes that Mr. Grimes at the Piggly Wiggly had given me the day before. As I wrapped slices of country ham, covered a big bowl of baked beans, tied a string around the boxes containing the deviled eggs and buttered salt-rising bread, I thought, Surely this will satisfy the hungriest of men.

By the time I was bathed and dressed, Mrs. Eastlin knocked at the door. " I'm glad you could come," I told her. " I don't worry when you're with the children." I gave her shoulder a pat and the white-haired mother's helper smiled at me.

She helped me load the boxes in the car, plus two huge coffeepots I'd borrowed from the church, and the paper bags with the tin plates and ten-cent-store knives and forks. As an afterthought, I threw two old blankets and a pillow on the back seat, then backed out of the driveway and headed for the job.

Dux had written down the route I was to take, but he always insisted on saying east, west, north, or south, instead of right or left, on the turns. I never did have any sense of direction. Dux thinks I ought to be able to " feel " which way I'm going, but I reckon I'm just dumb, so I always allow plenty of time for wrong turns. Driving down the river road, loving the gorgeous reds and browns of the trees, the pleasant sunshine that took the chill from the air, I thought, I'm the luckiest woman alive. I have everything — all I've ever dreamed of having: a pretty house, three wonderful children, and a husband who has what it takes and isn't afraid to stick his neck out.

As I turned on to the narrow, muddy lane that led down to the river, I could hear the engine of the boat and the clank-clank of the pipe. For once, I hadn't taken a single wrong turn, so it was only a little after five when I pulled up alongside the other cars.

The big old dredge boat looked like a live monster digging in the river, its huge hand lifting the mud and silt, carrying it over, and dropping it downstream. Two barges near the shore had skids spiked across the top to hold them apart, making a ramp that would be directly over the ditch. I'd watched Dux make drawings of how the job would be done; now I was seeing the real thing!

Men with mud-spattered woolen shirts and mucky leather boots carried pipe from the shore to the barges;

others swung picks in the ditch that went up the river-bank. It made me go weak to watch them work so feverishly. I began to wonder if I did have enough food, or even the right kind.

Jeff Nichols waved to me and started over to my car. He'd been Dux's right-hand man for a long time and was very dependable, but, like most pipeliners, he played as hard as he worked, which sometimes got him into trouble. Short, stocky, with an easy grin, he came up the muddy bank and doffed his battered cap in an exaggerated bow.

"Howdy, little lady," he greeted me, his eyes twinkling with the secret we shared. "Reckon we're aimin' to show the brass hats a thing or two, ain't we?"

"You bet we are," I said, thankful for Jeff and his loyalty. "What do the men think? Do they mind that Dux is going against orders?"

"Heck, no. They're gettin' a kick out of it. Shucks, I wouldn'ta missed this for nothin'. You sure got to hand it to that man of yours," he said.

I agreed with him one hundred per cent. "Where is Dux?" I'd been looking all around, but he wasn't in sight.

"He's out on the tug; got the dredge crew all hepped up," Jeff chuckled, "and they never knew him till to-day —" He broke off and pointed to a small motorboat coming in to shore. "Here comes the boss now."

Dux got out of the boat, pulled it up on shore, tied it to a willow tree, and climbed the slippery bank.

"Hi!" I called to him before he reached the car. "How's it going?"

"Not bad," he said. "When the pipe's loaded on the barge and the ditch up the bank is finished, we'll be ready for the shore bend — ought to get it in by tomorrow noon." I wondered how in the world they expected to bend that heavy-looking pipe.

He opened the door of our sedan and motioned to Jeff. " Take this food down on the barge. I hope it's enough."

" Sure smells good." Jeff sniffed as he lifted the Piggly Wiggly boxes, set them on the ground, and reached for the coffeepots.

" I don't think cold coffee will taste too good," I said, thinking how Dux liked it piping hot.

" We'll heat that on the salamander," Jeff answered as he lifted the big pots, slopping coffee on the car. " What're those blankets and pillows for? "

" Well, I thought maybe Dux could take a nap," I said.

" Yeah? " Jeff looked at Dux and grinned. " Yeah? " He chuckled as he picked up a load of food and sloshed down the riverbank.

" Shortie, I've made arrangements for the cook on the dredge to feed the men tomorrow and Sunday," Dux said, and added, " Now don't be hurt — it's just that I think they need hot food."

" But I wanted to help," I said, feeling let down but a little relieved too.

" You can." He fished a slip of paper out of his shirt pocket and held it out. " Get these groceries and bring them in the morning." He leaned inside the car and kissed me. " You do help, sweet — just believing in me." He looked at me, smiling that sudden, sweet smile, and I thought, No wonder I'm putty in his hands.

The next morning I got out to the job in time to watch them bend the pipe to make it fit the ditch. I wondered why they didn't do it the other way around, but Dux says it's cheaper to bend the pipe. Several joints had been screwed together, and things that Jeff later said were weights, and collar-leak clamps were put around the pipe where the joints came together. Then the whole thing was suspended between the barges and the riverbank.

The part on the bank rested on skids with its end sticking up and chained to the pipeline that had been laid to the river. The other part was in the ramp between the barges. In the middle two men straddled the pipe and were given firewood, which they placed in iron cradles fastened around the pipe. They poured coal oil over the wood, slid off, and touched each stack of firewood with a burning rag tied to a stick.

The fire flared up and burned furiously. On top of the riverbank, a winch truck lifted the pipe slowly while men jerked the skids out from across the ditch. Then they moved to one side and watched the red flames licking at the pipe.

Everyone stood still. For minutes there was no sound except for the chug-chug of the dredge boat out in the river and the crackling of the burning wood.

Then, amazingly, the suspended pipe started to sag from the heat. Jeff watched intently, his eyes never leaving the pipe, and slowly raised his arms. Suddenly, he jerked them down and yelled, " Let 'er *go!* "

The winch dropped the pipe down into the water, the fire went out, and I began to breathe again. In a few moments the pipe was raised once more, the cradle things removed, then gently lowered into its final resting place in the bottom of the ditch.

I got out of the car, picked my way around the sticky, reddish mud thrown up from the ditch, and walked over to where Dux and Jeff were standing.

" Couldn't be better. She fits like a glove," Jeff was saying. " Pipe gang'll kick off right after chow — " He broke off as a car stopped on top of the riverbank. " That'll be the new stabber."

" Well, who's going to get stabbed? " I laughed.

Dux turned around. " Hello, honey. He means pipe-

26

stabber, the guy who tells the pipe gang when to lower or raise until the joint is true in the collar and won't cross-thread," he explained, and turned back to Jeff. " Take the groceries out of her car and get the men started to the dredge. It's about time to eat."

" I've got some sandwiches and a bottle of milk in the car, enough for both of us," I said, hopefully.

Dux shook his head. " I want to eat with the men, Shortie. We've got things to talk about."

" But isn't everything going all right? " I asked, thinking he did look worried, or maybe just tired.

" Yes, it's going fine — but I've got to keep it that way." He took my arm, helped me around the mud to the car and opened the door. " If this weather holds, we haven't got a thing to worry about." He half pushed me in the car, gave my cheek an absent-minded pat, and closed the door. " I'll come back after a while and take you out on the barge, show you how it's done."

I ate my sandwich, drank some milk, and sat wondering why men would choose this rough, dirty work. But Dux says construction gets in your blood. Good fresh air, free sunshine, good fellowship — a sort of share-and-share-alike brotherhood. Even to sharing the single dipper in a bucket of drinking water, I'd noticed. I bought Dux one of those cute little collapsible drinking cups to carry in his pocket, but for some reason he'd never use it.

The men went back to work and pretty soon I saw Dux motion to me. I put on my gloves, buttoned up my coat, and went down the mucky riverbank to the tug. I'd been out on a few of the pipelines Dux had built, but this was my first real close-up of a water crossing and I thought of what I would tell Mrs. Higgins. Nearly every month at our guild meeting, she'd fuss about her three- or four-dollar gas bill. I wished she could see how these men knocked themselves out just so she could bake a pie without shoveling coal or chopping wood.

We rode the tug out into the muddy Ohio, climbed aboard the dirty barge, and walked over to where the men were working. Dux leaned down to me and pointed to a pile of pipe stacked on the barge.

"First, they take one of those joints with carrying tongs," he said in a voice loud enough to be heard over the noise, " and stab it into the collar. I told you this morning how the stabber does that. Then the jack and growler-board men set the jack to support the pipe and hold it steady." He pushed me closer. " Watch these two men."

I watched, and suddenly they threw a rope around the pipe, pulling it in such a way that the joint started to roll so fast it was almost a spin.

" When it's as tight as they can make it," Dux said, " the tong gang and collar-pounder take over."

" What's a collar-pounder? " I asked, raising my voice above the noise.

" Just that," he said. " He pounds the collar with a hammer to tell each of the tongs when to work — we say he ' strokes them.' " He straightened up, crammed tobacco into his pipe, cupped his hands to light it, and flipped the match into the water. " Three sets of heavy lay-tongs are thrown over the pipe," he went on, " and at the stroke of the hammer, each tong works alternately so that the joint is kept rolling continuously until it gets too tight for one tong — there they go."

We watched the pipe go round and round, each group of tong-men working to the beat of the hammer with a sort of rhythm in their movements. Dux leaned closer and said in my ear: " Listen to the pounder when he double raps. There now — all tongs work together. He's feeling the heat of the collar with his other hand. There! Now all

28

three tighten together until he raps them off."

The noise had subsided somewhat since all of them started working in unison. Dux said, "It's got to be exactly right; otherwise it will gall or pull the threads and cause a leak."

When they stopped, I could see some "threads" on the pipe and I pointed them out to Dux, eager to show my newly acquired knowledge.

He knocked his pipe against his hand. "That's all right," he grinned. "Mike knows his business. Some joints go in farther than others."

They had just finished putting on the clamps when the tug came back for us and I asked Dux why they were needed if the joints were tight enough to keep the water out.

"Just as an added precaution," he said as we walked across the barge toward the tug. "Collars are put on the pipe at the mill and doped with fast-drying lead. If the back-up tong — that's used to hold the collar steady — happens to slip and move the mill side of the collar, the clamp will keep it from leaking."

I was quite impressed and more than a little in awe of my husband's knowledge, wondering for the hundredth time why he still envied men with college diplomas. He works so hard, I thought, he studies so much, and he's the boss of all these men. Most of them are older too. I smiled, remembering when he was first put in charge of the transportation department. He started to grow a mustache to make him look older, but the darned thing grew lopsided, and anyway I didn't like it, so he finally shaved it off.

It was getting on toward late afternoon when we left the tug and climbed the bank toward the car. Grayish billowy clouds floated across the sun and Dux kept looking toward the sky.

" I don't like the looks of them," he said. " Those clouds could mean a storm. Could mean trouble."

" Oh, no! " The chill that ran down my spine had nothing to do with the air. Dux had studied the weather when he learned to fly and now, after several years of being in the Air Reserves, he was nearly always right in his predictions.

" Well, maybe not." He gave me a quick kiss and hurried back to the tug, calling over his shoulder for me to drive carefully.

I slid under the wheel and drove slowly toward home, my thoughts whirling with the enormity of the job. I hadn't dreamed it was so big. What if a storm did come? What if the Company found out and fired Dux before he could finish? I shuddered and felt a sudden hollowness in my stomach.

As I pulled in our driveway and got out of the car, I looked up at the high, streaky clouds, the faint pink around the sunset, and sighed with relief. It didn't look like a storm to me — or was it only wishful thinking?

I let Mrs. Eastlin go home, gave my cherubs their supper, told them a story, and put them to bed. Then, wondering what we'd do if Dux did get fired, I went down to my storeroom to check the groceries and see what I really did have. Half a case of beans, a few cans of corn, four jars of blackberry jam Mother had sent us, and the country ham with a big chunk cut off. Not much, I thought, and frowned.

It won't take Dux long to get another job, I told myself as I undressed for bed. He can do practically anything, so I'm not going to worry.

3

JUST BEFORE DAYLIGHT I was awakened by a flapping blind and got up to close the window. My breath caught in my throat. It was pouring rain. Flashes of lightning streaked across the sky. Treetops near the house bent with the wind.

"Please, God," I whispered, "don't let anything happen to the job."

Pulling the blinds down to the sill, I crawled back into the warm bed, but sleep wouldn't come. I kept thinking of Dux and the cold, wet river, so I finally got up and went downstairs. For a long time I sat huddled in his favorite chair by the window, my feet tucked under me, watching the bleary yellow street lights and listening to the dreary rain beating against the panes.

I got the children up early, hurried them through breakfast, fixed an extra bottle for the baby, grabbed fresh didies, baby blanket, and pillow, put them all in the car, and drove out to the job, much to the delight of Buddy and Lee. I didn't want them to miss Sunday school, but I had to know what was going on and, anyway, Dux would need the dry clothes I was taking him. The sun was shining and there wasn't a sign of the storm until we got to the dirt road and splashed through the deep puddles.

I heaved a sigh of relief when I saw the men still working and the barges almost to the Indiana shore. Two men were doing something to a compressor nearby and, at my call, one of them came over to the car.

" Did the storm do any damage? " I asked.

" Don't think so," he said, lifting his cap and smoothing his thatch of unruly reddish hair. " Hard to tell yet. Barges kept rollin' and swingin' the pipe — boss finally told us to bull-plug the end and drop it on bottom." He looked serious.

" Is that bad? "

" Well, I reckon it ain't good," he said hesitantly. " Nothin' else to do, though. When a storm hits, she hits. Boss said he hoped he didn't wait too long to drop the pipe."

I looked out across the river. There wasn't a chance of seeing Dux. " I'll leave these clothes with you," I told the man, giving him the things I'd brought for Dux. " I'm going home. Please tell my husband to call me if there's anything he wants."

I drove to the church, parked around the corner, let Buddy and Lee out and waited for them, meanwhile changing the baby and giving her a bottle. I kept the engine running and the heater on, for the air was cool in spite of the warm sun. After the children came back, we stopped at a drugstore, bought ice-cream cones for us all, and went home.

It was a long afternoon. I baked a devil's food cake and made a pecan pie, using nuts that Dux had shelled for me Thursday night. It seemed a year ago. If everything went according to schedule, he would be coming home sometime tonight. Finally I went to bed and slept fitfully.

But Dux didn't come home Sunday night. He didn't come home Monday morning. By noon I couldn't stand it any longer and called Mrs. Eastlin. She couldn't come at once and I waited impatiently for her.

It was after two o'clock when I started out to the job. I knew something was wrong when I saw Dux and six or seven men standing idly by the compressor. He came over as soon as I stopped the car.

" What's wrong? " I asked, shocked at the tired lines in his face, the dark circles under his eyes.

" Got a leak." He slid into the front seat beside me. " That storm played hob." He took off his cap and ran his hands through his hair. " We hooked up the compressor, couldn't get more than forty pounds pressure, so we know there's a leak," he said wearily.

" What'll you do? " I asked, feeling as empty as an unused glass jar.

" Captain Wilks sent for a professional diver. Jeff and I ran the motorboat over the ditch until we saw bubbles. Then we moved the barges over the spot and rigged up an air pump. Now we're just waiting till the diver gets here."

He lighted a cigarette, tossing the match to the ground with a nervous motion. " And that's not all that's wrong." He drew a grim breath and went on: " Addison is back. He came down this morning and brought two men."

" Oh, Dux! " I gasped. " What did he say? "

" Nothing — yet. I managed to keep busy on the other side of the barge. Jeff took them around; said the men came down to look the site over; said Addison's face was a thundercloud and he heard him muttering to himself." He tossed the half-smoked cigarette away and leaned his head on the back of the seat.

Oh, I thought wildly, Dux won't have a chance to resign. They'll fire him outright. " Maybe Addison won't come back," I said.

Dux shook his head. " He probably will. I only hope we

33

get the leak fixed before he does."

There was a line on his cheek that I'd never seen before and I traced it gently with my finger. " You look so tired, honey. Didn't you get any sleep at all? "

" Some," he said absently, letting his head fall against my shoulder. " Wish that diver would show up."

" Maybe you can take a nap while you're waiting," I said, pushing the damp hair back and stroking his forehead.

Dux smiled faintly. " Fat chance. I'm more tired mentally than I am physically. We've all been taking turns cat-napping on the dredge. This waiting hurts."

A car pulled up not far from us and Dux sat up. " Here he is. Come on — you can go over to the barge with me."

When we got on the barge, I watched Dux's men put the underwater outfit on the diver, the heavy shoes, walk him over to the ladder, and put the grotesque helmet over his head. Then they fastened the weighted belt around him and he went down the ladder into the water.

It seemed only a few minutes before he came back in sight, motioned for the men to unfasten the helmet, which they did. Then he said: " This suit leaks. You've got to get another one if you expect me to do your work."

Dux motioned to Jeff. Moving closer to them, I heard Dux say: " That's the only suit we could get. I think he's stalling anyway. Get rid of him. Have someone get a cold-patch kit from one of the trucks and fix those leaks."

I wanted to ask who'd go down if they let the diver leave, but no one was paying any attention to me, so I stood and watched, wondering what Dux would do. He was a man who worked for results and he didn't stop till he got them, so I knew he'd get around this predicament somehow.

Somebody said, " Suit's ready." Dux left the group he was talking to and walked over to the man with the suit.

Suddenly, I realized his intentions. Oh, no, I thought wildly, he can't! He mustn't! But he was climbing into the diver's suit. I took a step forward, my hand over my mouth to stifle the words I wanted to call out to him. He looked up, met my eyes, and motioned to me. I walked slowly toward him.

"Don't worry. I know what I'm doing," he told me.

I nodded, not daring to speak, for fear I'd shame him in front of his men. But I did worry — any wife would. He'd told me once that he'd assisted divers at Sheepshead Bay and had gone down several times to do minor salvage jobs on sunken boats. But that was years ago, so it didn't lessen my anxiety.

Running to the side of the barge, I watched him go down the ladder, step by step. Two men stood near: one fed him the life line, the other fed him the air line. The water bubbled over his helmet and the sight chilled my heart. In a few minutes — or hours — he came part way up the ladder, motioning the men to open the face-door of the helmet. He told the men what was wrong — something about a clamp, explained what tools he'd need, arranged for a set of signals, smiled at me, and went back down.

Once again, watching the bubbles close over him, I almost choked with fear. Everyone was quiet. The only noise was the squeal of the wheel as it turned, pumping the life-giving air to my husband. I dug my trembling fingers into the palms of my hands as I prayed silently.

Then Dux signaled and a tool was lowered to him. Soon we could hear the muffled sound of the tool against the pipe. It seemed forever that we stood staring down into the muddy water, watching the bubbles, listening to the muffled clank of iron against iron.

Finally Jeff spoke, his voice loud in the stillness. "He's signaling to be pulled up."

I went weak with relief, wiped the perspiration from my face, and tried to swallow the lump in my throat. The men helped Dux onto the barge, unfastened the helmet, and someone stuck a lighted cigarette between his lips. He was blue with cold and the cigarette trembled from his chattering teeth. I turned away, biting my lips. I didn't want these men to see me cry.

Jeff threw a blanket around Dux as they pulled the suit off, spilling water over the floor. He was soaked to the waist. They led him to the salamander, red-hot now, and kept the blanket around him while Jeff got him into dry clothes — all talking at once. It was as if they were statues suddenly come to life.

When he was dressed and buttoned up in extra sweaters, Dux came over and put his arm around me. " Smile at me, sweet. Don't look so glum."

" I was scared to death," I whispered, groping for his hand.

" I was afraid you would be." He gave my hand a squeeze, then turned to Jeff. " Let's go. I'm anxious to get that compressor going."

We went back to the Kentucky side of the river. I left the men and waited in the car, hoping with my whole being that the leak was fixed. I just couldn't go through that again. But I was so proud of my husband it hurt. I could tell the men were impressed too. Dux didn't value himself nearly enough, and I thought, Whatever his next job is, the company that gets him will be lucky.

" It's O.K." Dux got in the car, turned the ignition key, and started the motor. " Pressure built up to a hundred. So far, it's holding. Jeff'll call me in the morning." He waved to the men as we drove away.

" You mean it's really finished — completely done? " I asked, hardly daring to believe it.

His face moved, as if he wanted to say something and his voice wouldn't come, but when he did speak, all he said was, " Completely done."

We rode in silence. I knew my Dux. When I looked at the decisive line of his jaw, the wide, mobile mouth that was now a grim line, I could tell almost to a word what he was thinking. He wasn't happy in spite of all he had accomplished, in spite of proving his ability, even in spite of saving the Company thousands of dollars, which he probably had done. He liked Mr. Addison and Mr. Lewis, the president, and they had been good to him — like that time last winter when the baby was sick and we couldn't get any help. Mr. Addison had told Dux: " Go on home and help Winalee. We'll look after your work." And now, by acting in defiance of their wishes, he had let them down. I slid over close to him, leaned my head against his hard shoulder and didn't mind the grimy, sweaty work jacket.

The next morning Dux was up and dressed before the alarm went off. I dressed quickly and hurried to the kitchen just as the telephone rang and he answered.

In a few minutes he came in with a pencil and a sheet of paper in his hand, and sat down at the table. " That was Jeff on the phone. Everything's O.K. Now I've got to write this resignation." He rolled the pencil through his hands and looked thoughtfully at the ceiling.

I squeezed oranges, put bacon under the broiler, started the baby's cereal, then poured coffee for Dux, which he left untouched. He chewed his lip, staring at the blank sheet of paper, and there was a quality of forlornness about him that almost broke my heart. For five years he'd lived and breathed for the Gas Company, and now it was hard to say good-by. Why, I thought, it's like divorcing someone you love, and a surge of blinding anger went through me to think that Dux should have to suffer when he'd worked so hard, accomplished so much.

Turning off the gas in the oven and under the cereal, I went upstairs, washed and dressed the children, and brought them down to breakfast.

Dux looked up, smiled at the youngsters, who were strangely quiet, as if they sensed that something was wrong, and started to write. After a while, he glanced at the clock over the stove, gulped down his coffee, and reached for his hat and coat on the rack. " I won't have time for breakfast. I want to get to the office before Addison does." He kissed the children and grinned at me as he wiped cereal from his mouth.

" Call me just as soon as you can " — I put my arms around him — " and don't worry, Dux."

He nodded, put on his topcoat, and went out the back door.

Every time the telephone rang, I jumped. I waited all morning, my mind whirling with a million thoughts. Finally, toward noon, he called.

" Shortie," he began, and I tried to tell from his voice how he was feeling, " it's all right. I'll tell you tonight."

" But, Dux, what happened? " I said in exasperation.

" Can't talk now. We're going out to the job. But it's all right," he repeated, and the line went dead.

Oh, I thought, wouldn't you *know* a man would think just saying " all right " covered everything! I slammed the receiver on the hook and blinked back blinding tears of resentment.

Somehow I got through the day. Dinner was ready and waiting when Dux got home a little before six. I had given the children an early supper and settled them upstairs with watercolor paints — a rare treat that would keep them busy for hours.

When I heard the car in the driveway, I flew to the door.

Dux grabbed me around the waist and whirled me around. It was good to see a smile on his face. I pushed him down on a chair, flung his hat to the floor, and plunked myself on his lap.

" Now," I said, " tell me every tiny detail."

" Well — " he settled himself more comfortably in the chair — " I was waiting in Addison's office when he got in. He glared at me, said I was fired. I told him no, because my resignation was on his desk. Then he told me how many kinds of a chump I was to go against orders. I said I was sorry to do it that way, but at least no man could say now that I couldn't do a river job. I started to leave his office and he yelled where did I think I was going. I said, ' Home.' Then he told me that Mr. Lewis wanted to see me — "

" Oh, golly — the president! " I breathed.

Dux nodded. " Mr. Lewis said I'd caused them much embarrassment. I'm sorry about that. Then he said that if I'd failed on the job, he would surely have fired me." He ran a hand through his hair, grinned down at me, and I waited impatiently for him to go on.

" But since the job is O.K. — well, Lewis said, they wanted to hold onto a man with initiative. Now, baby, let me get this coat off. I'm hot."

I wanted to laugh and cry, but I hugged Dux tight around the neck, kissed him on the lips, and got up from his lap.

" I probably shouldn't tell you this," I said happily, " but I think you're just wonderful! "

4

LIFE WITH DUX hasn't been a perennial picnic, but it has never been dull. We've been shunted from pillar to post. We've basked in clover, and we've robbed the children's piggy banks. As with most married couples, we've had our ups and downs, with emphasis on the downs, but through it all we've clung together.

Secretly, I've known from the start that Dux is my better half, but I don't think he realizes it. At least he is too much of a gentleman to say so. He's the patient, easygoing type, and idealist, tender and loyal, with a possessive pride in his own, while I am an impulsive scatterbrain who flies off the handle, and have been known on occasion to throw things. I'm not proud of it, but some people have to learn about life the hard way.

In moments of fury I'm likely to say things that will take me weeks to get over feeling sorry for. But Dux understands me, thank goodness. I've a sneaking suspicion that if I'd married anyone else, I'd have been thrown out on my ear. If only there were some foolproof way a girl could learn to be a good wife and mother before her marriage!

About the only briefing I had was from Abigail Thompson, my English teacher at boarding school. Years before,

Mrs. Thompson's artist husband had killed himself — some said because of a bad painting, others thought it was strong drink. But "Miss Abby," as we called her, blamed herself. Obviously she had made up her mind that we girls should profit through her mistake.

She never missed an opportunity to talk to us about marriage, with accent on those finer qualities that go to make a good wife. A casual word dropped now and then in class would start her off on her favorite subject — much more vital than English to teen-agers. And certainly more intriguing.

We adored Miss Abby. Always immaculate in black silk, with a white tatted-lace collar, she'd stand straight and tall beside her desk, blue-veined hands clasped in front of her, her voice low but intense.

" The average bride holds her groom in the palm of her hand," she would say. " She is foolish if she doesn't keep him there. *Men* may differ, but all *husbands* are alike! They need sympathy, love, and praise." Her faded blue eyes would deepen with earnestness. " No man can succeed in his chosen field without the faith of the woman he loves."

We'd sit on the edge of our seats, exulting in the power of woman, straining our ears to hear more. Once, she threw the whole class into a dither when she said daringly:

" To make a success of your marriage, girls, you must be three women to your husband: a wife, a mother, and a — er — a mistress." Quick color dyed her face, for those were the hush-hush days when mothers tried to keep their daughters innocent — and ignorant.

We girls discussed that audacious remark in private and it bothered us no end. In fact, it was so confusing that we could hardly sleep nights and we'd slip into one another's rooms, push a rug against the door so that the lights wouldn't show, stuff the keyhole with cotton, and talk for hours. But not one of us ever had the courage to ask Miss Abby how we'd know when to be which!

She blamed broken marriages on the woman, giving tragic examples of wives who turned the holy state of matrimony into endurance tests. As case histories she cited the overly meticulous housekeeper who drove her husband away from a house so clean that it was no longer a home; the overly conscientious young mother who neglected her spouse after the baby came; the jealous creature whose groundless suspicions wrecked her marriage.

It puzzled me. I couldn't remember my mother doing any of these things, yet my parents were divorced. I couldn't bring myself to talk about it to Miss Abby, for it was my private tragedy and the hurt hadn't healed. To be torn between the two people you love best in the world is a soul-shaking experience, especially if you are only thirteen.

That cold rainy day that Mother, my small brother Drexel, and I left Papa seemed the end of everything to me. Up until then Father, Mother, and God had been my trinity. They were so closely allied in my heart that it was difficult to separate one from the other two.

We stood on the station platform of the small Missouri town that had been our home for the past six years, waiting for the train that would take us away from Papa, away from friends, away from everything I had known and loved. It had always been fun visiting Grandma in West Liberty, Kentucky, but this was no visit. This time we were going to stay. A shiver ran through me, though I was not cold in spite of the damp March wind.

I looked at Papa — tall, thin, almost frightened-looking, his dark eyes staring at the railroad tracks as he held tight to Drexel's little hand. Then I looked at Mother. She stood apart from us, the wind whipping her skirts around her slender body, her eyes dark with misery, clutching our tickets in one gloved hand. The very silence that surrounded us was like something alive, eating into my heart. Surely they won't let this dreadful thing happen to us, I thought, and waited hopefully for tears that would soften Mother's grim lips, the reconciliation that would follow, and a happy ending to this terrible day.

The train whistled in the distance. Frantically, I clung to Papa. " I won't go," I sobbed wildly. " I won't! "

He let go of Drexel's hand, took me in his arms, and pressed his lips against my cheek. " It's best, sweetheart," he whispered hoarsely. " You're a big girl now. Go with Mother; she needs you."

I never felt smaller or more inarticulate in my life. I tried to say something, but the words wouldn't come. I tried to pray, but it seemed on that terrible day that God wasn't listening.

The train came to a hissing stop. Helplessly, I pushed through the passengers to a window and flattened my nose against the glass. The wheels began to turn. Swallowing the scream in my throat, I wiped the window with a soggy handkerchief and watched the blurred figure of my father fade into the distance.

Mother's people meant to be kind, but they didn't understand and they didn't appreciate Papa. I couldn't bear to talk about what had happened, so I shut myself into a world of my own, clinging only to my small brother. Drexel sensed my need for him, though he was barely six. Every day was an ordeal that must somehow be lived through, and my chaotic mind was full of worry for Papa, so far away and so alone.

In September I was sent to Hamilton, a small Kentucky boarding school for girls, and it was there that I met Miss Abby and listened to her homely philosophy. She opened a

43

whole new life for me, and I made a vow that if I ever did get married, I'd stick to my husband come hell or high water!

The year I was fifteen, another blow fell. Our class had just finished practicing for the May Day exercises. Chaddie Wilson, my roommate, and I were leaving the gym when we met Miss Cassler, the school secretary. " There's a special for you in the office, Winalee," she told me.

" See you later," I said to Chaddie and hurried to the office, breathless with anticipation. Special-delivery letters were rare things at Hamilton. With an exaggerated sense of importance, I tore open the envelope and began to read.

Suddenly, fiercely, I thrust the letter into my skirt pocket. Too stunned even to cry, I walked slowly up the stairs to my room, slammed the door, and threw myself across the bed.

" Honey, what's wrong? " Chaddie cried in a frightened voice.

I shook my head. I couldn't talk about it even to Chaddie. She left the room and I was thankful to be alone. The incredible had happened: Mother wanted to marry again. Still young enough to believe in miracles, I had never given up hope of going back to Papa, in spite of the divorce. Now, it would never be.

I thought of the fun we used to have, the games we played. I recalled the time Papa had taken me on one of his short business trips. I was in seventh heaven! How I loved the brightly lighted hotels, the shopping sprees, the moving pictures! But most of all, I'd gloried in the grown-up way Papa treated me.

I thought of the times we'd spent in the kitchen when Mother went shopping or to the Ladies' Aid Society. Papa liked to cook. He would tuck a big towel into the belt of his pants — Mother's aprons were much too small — and

44

he'd dirty every pan in the kitchen, turning out concoctions that no one had ever heard of. But Drexel and I thought he was wonderful and gleefully ate everything he cooked.

Those were happy times. I felt safe and secure — and loved. Now, it was all over. A great black wave seemed to fold over me, sucking me down, and I buried my head in the pillow and sobbed — long, convulsive, bitter sobs.

I felt a hand on my shoulder and looked up to see Miss Abby sitting on the edge of the bed. " What is it, dear? Chaddie said you've had bad news."

Without answering, I took the letter from my pocket and gave it to her. The hateful words kept beating at my brain: " So we'll wait until you get home," Mother had written. " It will be a small wedding with just the family."

Miss Abby pulled me up to her, cradled my head against her shoulder, and wiped my swollen eyes with her handkerchief. Between sobs, I poured out the whole story and she listened without a word until I finally stopped from sheer exhaustion. She smoothed my rumpled hair with a gentle hand and began to talk in a soft, soothing voice.

For an hour she talked to me about Mother's need for love and companionship, about my responsibility toward her happiness, and about life in general. Too tired and heartsick to argue, I promised to write Mother at once and tell her only how much her happiness meant to me.

Two months later they were married in front of the fireplace in Grandma's parlor, with its stiff lace curtains, the fragrance of wilting roses, and the smell of furniture polish. I was Mother's only attendant and, for all my inner turmoil, I felt proud of her. If only Papa could see her now, I thought, childishly.

She really was a perfect bride. She looked pretty and girlish in the blue crepe de Chine, the exact color of her shining eyes, wisps of brown hair curling up over her matching turban, as she smiled at the man standing beside her. He wasn't tall like Papa, but his shoulders were broad in the coat of his immaculate white suit and he looked as if he were used to exercise. His white hair, brushed close to his well-shaped head, revealed the years, but there was something boyish in the way he looked at Mother.

The wedding service seemed endless. But finally the last prayer was said, the padlock snapped shut, and Mother was another man's wife. I kept my promise to Miss Abby and didn't cry, but there was a sickish panic in my stomach and I could not swallow the lump in my throat.

Drexel and I stayed with Grandma and Grandpa during the three weeks' honeymoon. They were good to us, insisting on the candy pulls, parties, and things we'd always loved before, but I felt like a doll whose sawdust has run out, leaving it limp and useless. I even thought of running away, but there was no place to go. Papa hadn't answered my last letter telling him of Mother's marriage and, since he didn't stay in one place very long, I had no idea where he was.

The dreaded day came when they returned from their honeymoon. Drexel and I stood on the porch of the new house, his hot little hand holding tight to mine, and watched Mother's husband laughingly pick her up, carry her over the threshold, and set her down on the other side. Then he came back toward us. Before I realized his intentions, he had swept me up in his arms and carried me through the door, saying over his shoulder to Drexel:

" Come on, Son. We've got to help our girls unpack and get settled in our new home."

Neither Drexel nor I could help loving this man we soon learned to call Dad. " Lucky " Baldwin, as he was called by his friends, possessed a deep understanding for his fellow man, and it didn't seem odd at the time that I could talk to him about Papa. Once he said, "Your father must have been a wonderful man to have inspired such love and loyalty in a daughter," and added wistfully, "I've envied men with children."

I never forgot my father. But I did get over feeling disloyal to him as we gradually settled down to a normal, happy family life.

Dad was superintendent of the mountain division of a utility company and sometimes walked the pipelines himself. During the summer I loved to go along, and we'd often walk miles, coming home with our arms full of daisies, honeysuckle, and wild roses. I loved the Kentucky hills, our clean little town nestled in the valley, the lazy Licking River winding in and around, where we used to catch bass and catfish, and swim if the rain didn't make it too muddy.

We had fun too. Even if we did have to make it ourselves. We had hay rides, slumber parties, picnics, rode horseback, and once a week we had movies. That is, we had movies if the tunnel didn't fall in and delay the mail train bringing the films.

Our branch railroad was like a tired old lady, always dropping things, for the worn-out cribbing of the tunnel let the dirt and rocks fall onto the tracks. It always happened at the wrong time, upsetting the even tenor of our lives and causing the harassed trainmen to forget their religion. The coaches carried picks and shovels for this emergency, and passengers were often required to dig themselves out.

Old Joe Ed Mitchell, paralyzed from the waist down, ran the motion-picture machine. The fact that he was in a wheel chair didn't keep him from being an expert at splicing old, used films — the only kind we ever seemed to get.

When the schoolhouse burned down, Joe Ed bought the bell, saying: " Now, when I'm ready, I'll just ring the bell. Never know how long 'twill take me to fix them old fillums."

And so, with pomp and ceremony, the townspeople put up the bell in front of the town hall where we had our shows, and West Liberty became the only town in Kentucky, perhaps in existence, to call its patrons to the movies with a bell.

Sometimes, on hot summer nights, the film would break in the middle of an exciting picture and Joe Ed would call out in a disgruntled voice:

" Might as well go set on your porches where it's cool, folks. I'll ring the bell when I get the dang fillum fixed."

But if the night was cool, the audience would stay. The women would knit, the men unfold their newspapers, and we kids would scramble onto the stage and put on our own show. Music students would turn out everything from " The Rosary " to " Alexander's Ragtime Band " on the tinny old piano. Elocution pupils would recite " Curfew Shall Not Ring Tonight," " The Raggedy Man," or " Miss Minerva's Baby " with eloquent gestures. Our proud parents made an excellent audience and we didn't mind waiting for hours to see Pearl White escape from a peril or Mary Pickford shake her curls at the villain.

So, with boarding school in the winter and vacations in the summer, the years slipped by. Like all girls, I dreamed of a handsome husband who'd come driving a Stutz Bearcat and take me away to a beautiful home in the city — blissfully unaware that my Prince Charming would come riding Mr. Perry's old nag, Betsy, and that my first real home would be tents thrown together in the middle of an oil lease.

5

THE SUMMER I was eighteen I met Dux. It was June and the locust trees in front of our house were in bloom, the fragrance of their blossoms filling the air. It was also vacation time and I felt giddy with the sheer joy of being alive — and free.

It was good to be home. Good to get out of captivity. Hamilton advertised itself as " an exclusive school for young ladies," and it was — exclusive of all freedom and of anything with pants on, unless you counted bald-headed Professor McDermott or old Felix, the janitor.

Of course, every year we had two receptions to which the boys were invited — stiff, formal affairs that weren't much fun. Occasionally a male visitor, armed with a parental permit, would come to break the all-female routine. Then we'd sit in high-backed chairs in the plush drawing room, trying to say things that we didn't mind the teacher hearing as she sat in the hall outside the open doorway — a procedure much too discouraging to most young men, and not at all inspiring to most young ladies. It was no wonder that we girls were a bit boy-crazy and I always looked forward with breathless anticipation to the summers at home.

49

Mother had written that our town was to have a new branch railroad, that the work would start in June — and that was another reason for feeling giddy. Oh, not because of the new railroad; I didn't give a hoot about that — at eighteen, you don't. But fifteen young civil engineers were something to think about. They were being sent to do the survey and were expected any day. If you've ever been a girl in a small town, you'll understand what *that* meant! Cousin Lizzie Cox had told Mother that two of them were University of Kentucky students and classmates of Henry Clay Cox, her son and my favorite relative.

We were eating breakfast on the back porch when we heard the front door slam and Henry Clay came out. He always lighted up a room like an electric sign. His ready laugh, his confident bearing, and his way of making you like yourself made him welcome anywhere.

" Hi, folks," he said cheerfully, pulling up a chair next to me. " You as glad to get home as I am, chicken? "

" I sure am," I said, admiring the way his hair curled in spite of his efforts to keep it slicked down.

" Get a plate for Cousin Henry Clay, Son," Mother said to Drexel.

" No, no, I've already had breakfast, Cousin Hattie," he said. " But I'll have a cooky. You always could make better cookies than anyone I know." Mother beamed as she passed the cooky plate.

" Engineers come yet? " Dad asked, glancing slyly at me.

" Yeah, that's what I came over to tell you," Henry Clay said between bites. " They all got in last night — right good-looking bunch of fellows. I'm rounding the gang up for a get-together tonight." He turned to me. " I've picked Bill Ellis for you, kid. He's a good guy, a frat brother of mine, great fun and a darn good dancer."

" Oh, golly," I breathed, tingling with excitement.

" You get your best bib and tucker on, sugar." He gave my shoulder a pat as he got up. " I'll bring Bill over about seven."

All that day I went around with my head in the clouds, practically dizzy with anticipation. I hurried through the breakfast dishes, dusted the furniture in the parlor, and washed my hair. Sitting in the sun while it dried, I ran fresh ribbons through the eyelet embroidery of my camisole and petticoat, pulled the bastings from the hem of the blue dress Mother had just finished making, and let my imagination run wild.

Hours ahead of time I began to get dressed, piling my hair on top of my head in a Psyche knot, buttoning the new high-heeled slippers that pinched only a little but made me look inches taller, buffing my nails till they shone. At six thirty I was ready. I loved the new georgette with its accordion-pleated skirt, just perfect for dancing, the long sash, and tiny rhinestone buttons. Looking in the mirror, I wished again that I could have one of the new little pots of rouge, but when I'd asked Mother she'd looked at me with such horror that I'd never mentioned it again. But excitement had reddened my cheeks and I rummaged in the back of a dresser drawer, pulled out a small bag of cinnamon drops, and made my lips a glistening red.

" Need any help, honey? " Mother came into my room and I pirouetted around, stopping in front of her for inspection. She stared at me for a moment and suddenly, surprisingly, there were tears in her eyes. But all she said was, " You look so much older with your hair up."

" That's the idea," I laughed, giving her a hug with a feeling of gratitude that I could never put into words. " Don't you think the blue in my dress makes my eyes darker? " I asked, peering into the mirror.

She nodded, yanked the sash toward my middle, and

perked up the bows. Dad called from the hall below, " You've got company, kitten."

I caught my breath, gave Mother a peck on the cheek, grabbed the china silk scarf from the bed, and ran nervously down the stairs.

Henry Clay and a dark, handsome boy, whom he introduced as Bill Ellis, stood at the foot of the stairs. Henry Clay's whistle gave me confidence and, as we went out the door, I felt a bright, dazed foreknowledge that this magic night would be one to be remembered.

The party was everything I'd dreamed. The exhilarating cut-in dances, the admiring glances of the boys, their gay nonsense, all added up to an evening that was perfect. Except for the boy at the piano whom Henry Clay introduced as Dux Gentry. He hardly noticed anyone — just sat there calmly playing ragtime, his right foot beating a rhythmic tattoo on the floor. Even when he was introduced, he just bobbed up from the stool, bowed, and scarcely missed a note, as if that piano meant more to him than any girl. Oh, he was good, but the phonograph would have done as well, and I kept hoping he'd dance. But he didn't, not once.

He wasn't tall, but he had the figure of an athlete, brown hair that fell into his eyes as his head nodded with the rhythm of the music, and hazel eyes that crinkled at the corners when he smiled, which was most of the time. His hands were big, but his fingers ran lightly over the keys, his whole body seemingly a part of the music.

When Cousin Lizzie called us to the dining room for cake and ice cream, I managed to sit by him. He wouldn't talk about himself, though, and he was different in other ways from anyone I'd ever met. He didn't seem interested in anything but impersonal things — such as the hidden moonshine stills he'd heard about, Kentucky thoroughbreds, and the homemade ice cream he was eating. But I did learn that he got his nickname, " Dux " — he pronounced it " Dukes " — from a sailboat he used to have on Sheepshead Bay in Brooklyn; though I'd flunked Latin, I did remember that it meant " leader."

When the party broke up at eleven, I invited the gang to our house the following Sunday night, making a mental note to lock our piano and hide the key!

That summer, June and July went by like fireflies in a flower garden. Dux and I were together a great deal. We danced to the phonograph music, picnicked on Daisy Knob, went on moonlight hay rides, sitting snugly close in the sweet-smelling hay, and walked together beneath a million stars. I was never so happy in my life. It was a summer of dreams come true.

Nobody wanted me to marry Dux, maybe even including Dux, but he couldn't help himself. Not after that night we slipped away from the gang to sit in the swing on our front porch. There was a full moon in the August sky, the scent of honeysuckle in the air, and strains of " The Missouri Waltz " drifted through the open window. We didn't talk, just sat swinging slowly back and forth, and I wondered what he was thinking.

Then his arm, resting on the back of the swing, slid down around my shoulders and he pulled me close to him. I caught my breath. Dux had never kissed me. In the beginning when he'd tried it, I'd told him primly that I didn't like that sort of thing and he believed me. It was Henry Clay's fault. In an older-brother manner he'd warned me against letting boys kiss me — unless I was sure it was love. So I'd waited for this moment.

I swallowed twice and lifted my face. He kissed me gently. Then his arms tightened around me and he kissed me like a man who has waited and waited. I felt as if I were floating, suspended in space.

" I love you," he said with his lips against mine.

" Oh, I love you too," I whispered, still breathless from the kiss.

" I wish I could ask you to marry me," he said later. " But I can't. I haven't the right."

Startled, I looked at him. " But *why?* "

He put his head in his hands and didn't speak for a moment. " I can't hope to give you the things every girl wants. Without a college education — "

" Is *that* all? " I said, with a wild feeling of happiness and relief.

He straightened up and turned to me. " But you don't know how important a college degree is," he said. " It makes a difference even in getting a job." He shook his head. " No, it wouldn't be fair — but I'll never forget you! " He pulled me close.

I wrenched myself free. " If you think I'm going to be just a memory, you're crazy! " I choked. " I don't care about a little old diploma. You told me yourself how you study, how you've been taking correspondence courses. Oh, don't you know how wonderful you are? "

Dux swept me back into his arms. " My darling," he said huskily, " I love you so much. It's just that I want you to have the best, but if you're willing to wait — "

I stopped his words with a kiss. After that night, he didn't have a chance.

The next day I shocked my family with the sudden announcement that I was engaged, madly in love, that I wanted to be married instead of going back to school.

" You thought you were in love last summer — remember? " Mother pointed out dryly. " You even went steady for weeks with — "

" But this is different. This is real — and for keeps. No

one has ever made me feel like — like this," I added solemnly.

After several stormy sessions, I finally won and we set the date in December.

It's good I'm not superstitious, because so many things about our wedding went wrong. It started with the job. When the railroad survey was finished, Dux got another job in our county surveying coal lands, with the promise of two weeks off for our honeymoon. Four days before our wedding, he surprised me by telephoning that he'd be in at noon. At two o'clock he hadn't come, but I knew the condition of the roads after the last night's rain, so I didn't start to feel uneasy until the clock struck three.

The house bustled with activity. Relatives running in and out, telephone ringing, people coming to see the gifts, everybody laughing and talking. I was the only one who seemed to be worrying about Dux.

I ran up to my room, slammed the door, and stood motionless. The new suitcases waited in the closet. My lovely ivory satin wedding dress, which Mother had just finished making, hung from the top of the closet door swathed in a white sheet so that it looked like an eerie ghost suspended there. My heart beat alarmingly. What if something had happened? What if there'd been an accident? The roads at this time of year were terrible and Dux had a rented car last time. In a panic I moved to the window and stared down at the muddy street below.

Suddenly, the breath caught in my throat. I didn't know whether to laugh or cry. There came Dux, plodding along on an old sorrel horse, holding his suitcase in front of him, his dilapidated work hat pulled down over his head — looking like anything else in the world but a prospective bridegroom.

I turned, ran down the stairs and out the door, just as

he pulled up in front of the house and got gingerly off the horse. Half sobbing, I threw my arms around his neck and clung to him, not caring if the whole world was watching.

He held me close. " Sorry you worried, darling, I couldn't get to a telephone. Blamed car stuck in the mud, so I walked a mile to the Perrys' and borrowed this old nag." He tied the reins to a tree and slapped the horse on the flank. " Good old Betsy — she's got more sense than I have."

Arm in arm, we started to the house. At the door he pulled me back. " Wait a minute. I've something to tell you." His voice sounded serious and there was a worried look in his eyes.

" I — that is — could we put off our wedding for a little while? Just until — "

" What? " I stared at him, a feeling of emptiness coming over me. " What are you trying to say? Don't you love me any more? "

" Oh, darling — more than you'll ever know." His hand tightened around my arm. " But the job blew up. They told me last night — the company's broke."

" Oh, Dux! " My throat unlocked at last and tears of relief filled my eyes. " Don't ever scare me like that again."

" But our honeymoon! " He shook his head. " I wanted to take you home, to New York, to show you off to my folks. Now maybe we'd better save the money."

I kissed him. " What's money? Anyway, we'll have the hundred dollars Uncle Charlie's giving us for a wedding present and the money your father sent. Let's go on to your home; then you can get a job later."

He didn't look convinced, but I opened the door and we went into the house.

Dux's brother Arthur was coming from New York to be best man, and of course Chaddie would be my maid of honor. She lived in Lexington, so we made arrangements for them to meet there, pick up the flowers we'd ordered weeks before, and come up on the train together. I wanted so much for them to like each other — my best friend and my husband's brother. But I certainly never expected them to become so engrossed that they'd leave the flowers on the train! The train had gone when we discovered it. There wasn't another one until Monday and our wedding was set for Sunday, so there wasn't anything we could do.

I wanted to savor every minute of my wedding day, so that in later years I could live it over, could say to my children, "I remember well my wedding day — " But actually it was mostly a blur.

The house was in a frenzy of preparation, neighbors running in to help, belated wedding gifts arriving, everybody excitedly talking at once. But at last the hour came.

As we stood in the parlor, in front of the ribbon-wrapped lattice with hurriedly made artificial flowers stuck here and there, and said, "I do," I was conscious only of the man beside me and my own heartbeat in the hushed stillness. Then Chaddie lifted my veil and Dux bent to kiss me. Something in his face made me catch my breath. "Oh, please," I prayed, "let it always be like this. Let me always keep him happy."

After being kissed and congratulated by practically every man, woman, and child in town, we finally cut the cake, had our pictures taken, and it was time to leave. I caught Chaddie's eye and lifted the ribbon-bedecked Bible, which I carried in lieu of a bridal bouquet, to throw straight at her — and remembered in time that it was Mother's!

We climbed in the hack, shaking the rice from our coats, and waved good-by. Mr. Willie Mack clucked to his mules and we were on our way to Index, three miles away and over a mountain. In the summer Mr. Willie used the Ford to and from the depot, but after the fall rains the mules were considered more dependable. On this propitious occasion, however, they chose to balk. Right in the middle of a huge mudhole!

" Ornery critters, mules," Mr. Willie said, shaking his head ominously. " Seems there's little a body can do when a mule makes up his mind."

He did everything short of building a fire under the stubborn beasts, but they wouldn't budge. Finally, he tied a piece of wire on the end of his whip and began to prod them.

" Giddap there, now, gol durn ye! " he yelled.

They pitched and they reared, but held their ground. I shuddered and shut my eyes when I saw a trickle of blood run down the rump of one. Then, with a sudden jerk that nearly broke our necks, they plunged through the mud and the hack went swaying and sliding down the road so fast that we had to hold onto the seat. We pulled up at the depot just in time to see the red lights of our train fade into the twilight. The last train until morning.

" Too bad," Mr. Willie said. " But I'll drive you over to Sayers'. They got an extra room for folks who miss the last train. Reckon they'll put you up."

At the white farmhouse, Mrs. Sayer fixed us a " bite of supper," which we scarcely touched, then led the way upstairs to the " spare " bedroom. A feeling of emptiness came over me, and suddenly all the exaltation disappeared; the dream burst, and I wished with all my heart that I were back home.

The room had white plaster walls, a matting rug on the floor, and a huge bed, covered with a patchwork quilt, which stood out from the wall. There was a steel engraving of *The Stag at Bay* hanging over the mantelpiece and, momentarily, I felt a strange kinship with the trapped animal.

Mrs. Sayer touched a match to the kindling in the small fireplace, pushed the rocker closer to the fire, saying, " Well, if there's anything you want, just yell," then went out and closed the door.

Dux and I were alone. He put his arms around me and I felt myself shrinking from him.

" Please don't," I choked, and walked blindly to the window. My hands felt icy and I was trembling inside. Was it because we didn't get to the Phoenix Hotel in Lexington, where we'd planned to spend the night? I wondered. Or had I made a horrible mistake? What did I really know about Dux? Marriage implied a terrible kind of intimacy, and I wasn't ready for it. I didn't know Dux well enough. I looked at him across the room and he must have read my thoughts.

" Darling, don't worry," he said. " It'll be all right. I'll go downstairs while you get undressed." He lifted my suitcase onto a chair, snapped the locks open, and raised the lid.

I couldn't find words, but I tried to smile gratefully. He smiled back, walked out, and closed the door softly.

I looked down at the suitcase and saw my bridal nightgown, white silk, with the fine lace yoke that Mother had crocheted, and a sickness settled inside me. Tonight I'd be claimed, expected to follow my husband into the strange and unknown. . . .

My mouth went dry as I moved to the suitcase, lifted the nightgown, and put it on the bed. Then, with trembling fingers, I unhooked my clothes and got undressed. I crawled between the cold sheets on the deep feather bed and pulled the covers over my head.

In a panic I heard the faint rustling as Dux got undressed. Then he pulled the covers away from my face and kissed me.

I sobbed. I couldn't help it. I felt like a child lost in the middle of a dark wood. Stop it! I told myself. This is Dux. You love him. It'll be all right. But when I looked at him, I saw only the face of a stranger.

Then I felt myself being lifted in his arms. He sat down in the chair in front of the fire and rocked me back and forth, his cheek resting on the top of my head. He talked of love, of life, and of God. Gradually I relaxed, happiness forming like a protective mantle over the fear and panic, and I wondered why I was ever afraid. This was Dux, *my* Dux. Our love was the most important thing in the world. As long as I had that I needn't ever be afraid of anything.

6

WHEN WE ARRIVED in New York and stood in line with the other passengers, waiting for the train to stop, once more I felt afraid. Dux had told me quite a lot about his family and I knew they must be wonderful people, but meeting your in-laws for the first time is somewhat of an ordeal. My hands felt icy. All the warmth, the happiness, the enchantment of the past few days seemed to vanish with this new reality. I groped for Dux's hand and found it.

He smiled down at me and winked. " Almost there."

I nodded and tightened my grip on his hand. The train lurched to a halt. We stepped off the car; Dux motioned to a porter who picked up our suitcases, and we followed him down the platform.

I swallowed and looked at Dux. " I'm scared, honey."

He laughed outright. " Not of my family — that's funny," he said. " Why, sweet, you'll love them! "

" Yes, I know — but will they love me? " I said ruefully.

He squeezed my arm. " Just you wait! "

We went up the stairs and through the doors into the huge Pennsylvania Station. Dux paused for a moment, looking around, and people pushed by us. " There's Mom and Papa," he said joyously, waving at an elderly couple who stood apart from the incoming crowd.

They looked very much as I had pictured them. A little on the stout side, a trifle old-fashioned, a sort of " togetherness " about them. Mr. Gentry held his wife's arm protectingly as they moved toward us. I'd have known she was Dux's mother, for she had that same engaging smile, her eyes crinkling at the corners.

" Oh, my dears," she cried as we reached them. She hugged us against her ample bosom, kissed us resoundingly, then dabbed quickly at her eyes. " I'm so glad, so glad! "

Dux's father kissed me on the cheek, shook hands with Dux, and said, " So, this is the little Kentuckian." Then he looked down at my feet and shook his head. " I'm disappointed."

Dux laughed and his mother said, " Now, now, Papa! " I tried to laugh, but it came out a little shakily.

" Well," his father went on, a grin on his wide mouth, " she's got shoes on — and hillbillys just don't wear shoes."

" Oh, we do when we go visiting," I said weakly.

He patted me on the shoulder and I breathed a sigh of relief.

We spent a week at Father and Mother Gentry's. They lived in a gracious, old-fashioned house and Dux's brother, and six sisters, four of whom were married, came to welcome us. I shall never forget the warmth of that welcome and the fact that both of Dux's parents took me into their hearts as one of their own. I liked to feel that it was because they were originally Southerners, like myself, Mother Gentry having hailed from Texas where Father Gentry had once been a Ranger. But that was before I came to realize that no one part of the world has a monopoly on kindliness.

Then Dux took a job making surveys for the Erie Railroad and we went to live in Rochester, New York. We stayed at a small family hotel for a while, but it was really too expensive. Anyway, I was dying to keep house. So we moved into an "efficiency" apartment, consisting of a furnished room with a studio couch, a bathroom, and a tiny makeshift kitchenette in what had obviously been a closet at one time. But I was thrilled, in spite of spending most of the daylight hours struggling with a poky old stove and incredibly complicated recipes. No matter how much time I spent, no matter how hard I tried, my dishes never even remotely resembled the beautiful pictures in the cookbooks. But Dux wasn't hard to please and so, with the help of a can opener, I managed fairly well.

One night I was looking in the icebox for the Mason jar of applesauce I'd made that morning to go with the spareribs boiling merrily on the stove, when Dux came in.

" You're early," I said, lifting my face for his kiss.

" Got a ride. Mr. Yates, the supervisor, brought me home in his car." He took off his coat and hung it in our closet. " That smells good. What do we eat tonight? "

" Spareribs, kraut, peas, and applesauce," I said, throwing a tea towel over the fallen, broken spongecake I'd forgotten to dump in the garbage can. " Did you have a nice day? "

" Not bad." He settled in the easy chair and I brought him a cup of coffee. " Say, sweet, how would it be if I asked Mr. Yates for dinner some night? "

"Oh, Dux, I can't cook well enough for your boss! " I didn't know Mr. Yates, but Dux had told me about his wife's death and how he lived all alone in a hotel.

He lifted the cup to his lips. " Sure you can. He's fed up with restaurant food. Anything home-cooked would taste good to him now. Let's make it Thursday. O.K.? "

I nodded, remembering one of Miss Abby's rules for a happy marriage: " Always smile when your husband asks guests to dinner — no matter who they are or how many."

Too bad she didn't teach us how to cook, I thought.

For the next three days I roamed around the neighborhood grocery stores, trying to make up my mind what to have to eat on Thursday night. Dux had said to keep it simple, but I did so want him to be proud of me. There's no telling what might come from entertaining your husband's boss, I reasoned, for Miss Abby used to talk about softening up the inner man with good food. So I bought freely, my mind resolutely closed to what was happening to the budget, and wondered how Mother used to get everything onto the table at once, still piping hot.

After Dux left for work on Thursday morning, I tied a towel around my head and went into a fever of preparations, cleaning, washing, and polishing everything in sight. At noon I was eating a hasty peanut butter sandwich when the doorbell rang. But it was only the mailman with a letter from Mother. Another " don't " letter probably, I thought, shoving it under some magazines to read later.

I went back to my sandwich, wondering what in the world was the matter with Mother. She kept telling me not to have a baby yet. The first time she'd written that, I'd supposed it was natural, because she used to say that a husband and wife ought to have plenty of time to get acquainted before the babies came. But when the opening sentence of her fifth letter said the same thing, I got mad and wrote her in no uncertain terms just the way I felt. I *wanted* babies — the sooner, the better. Ever since doll days I'd planned to have babies, lots of them. And lately I'd had reason to think we'd have to be choosing a doctor before too long. But I hadn't written that; I wanted to be sure first. Poor Mother, I thought: she's old. At her age you couldn't be expected to understand; you probably forgot how you felt at nineteen.

I could picture the folks when they got the news. Mother

would frown and say: " Shoot! I don't see why Winalee won't listen to me. She's too stubborn for her own good." But Dad's eyes would brighten; he'd grin and say, " Imagine *me* — a grandpop! "

Smiling at the picture, I happened to glance at the clock and suddenly came to life, gulped the last of my glass of milk, and went back to work.

After my last baking failure, I decided to buy a " store " cake and put chocolate fudge icing on it. It wasn't that I wanted to fool anyone — it was just that the bakery knew how to do the job better than I did. And it did look good when it was finished. Fudge was the one thing I knew how to make.

At five thirty everything was ready. The apartment shone and looked homey, in spite of the faded draperies, the dingy carpet, and the darns in the overstuffed chair. The gate-leg table sparkled with wedding-gift silver and linen — loot, Dux called them. The jonquils from our landlady's yard gave the room a festive air. She'd even offered to help with the dinner, but I wanted to do it all by myself.

I bathed and put on my prettiest dress, thankful for once that our clothes closet was in the bathroom, and went into the kitchen for a quick inspection. The beef roast in the oven sent out a mouth-watering aroma, the molded salad in the icebox had finally jelled, and the tomato soup in the long-handled kettle simmered on a back burner. That soup was my masterpiece. Grandma had sent me the recipe, writing out every step of the directions so that it was practically foolproof.

Satisfied, I walked into the other room just as a rat-a-tat-tat sounded on the door and Dux and his boss walked in.

" This is Mr. Yates, honey," he beamed. " My wife."

" H-hello," I stammered, staring at the dried-up hungry-looking old man with surprise.

" It's wonderful of you two young people to take pity on an old man," he said, getting out of his coat. " I'm surely going to enjoy a home-cooked meal."

I fervently hoped that he would — he looked as if he needed it.

Dux took his hat and coat, laid them on the back of the couch, and they sat down. " Excuse me," I murmured and fled to the kitchen.

In a minute Dux came in, swept me up in his arms, and kissed me. I tried to pull away. " You aren't supposed to leave a guest alone," I hissed.

" Couldn't kiss you in front of him." He bit my ear and held me tight. " Poor old Yates."

" Go back in there — I'll get the dinner on the table."

I broke away, pushed him through the door, and turned quickly. Too quickly. My elbow struck the handle of the soup kettle and sent it flying. I gasped and grabbed it before it hit the floor, but not until most of the soup had spilled. Gingerly, I stepped over the puddle, thinking I'd clean it up later, dished up two skimpy bowls and carried them into the other room.

" You two eat your soup while I take care of the rest of the dinner." I smiled weakly. " I don't care for any soup." I felt Dux looking at me, but I carefully avoided his eyes.

They sat down at the table and I went back to the kitchen. As the door swung behind me, I felt myself suddenly shoot forward and, before I knew what was happening, I'd landed smack-dab in the middle of the soup puddle. Tears of vexation filled my eyes and I looked up to see Mr. Yates and Dux at the open door.

" I f-fell in the soup," I stammered. " My dress, the

dinner, everything is r-ruined."

Dux gently helped me up and put his hand under my chin. "Don't you worry, dear. You're not hurt — that's all that matters. Change your dress. I'll clean this up. Nothing's ruined."

Then he laughed. They both laughed. "It's not f-funny," I snapped, going into the bathroom and letting the door slam behind me.

Mr. Yates probably thinks Dux married a nitwit, I thought, and tried to tell myself I didn't care. He was a funny-looking old man anyway.

When I came out, I found that Dux and Mr. Yates had taken up dinner and were waiting for me to sit down. We ate in embarrassed silence and I could feel my cheeks burn. The whole dinner tasted like so much cotton to me and I thought I must have cooked too much or else it tasted like cotton to them too, for most of it was left. I carried the dishes to the kitchen, refusing any help, dumped them into the sink, and cut the cake.

"She's worried for days," I could hear Dux saying softly. "Scared to death something would go wrong."

"It's only natural. I remember when we had our first company — " Mr. Yates began, but broke off when I came in with the cake.

The nightmare finally ended and Mr. Yates got up to leave. I wanted to say I was sorry the dinner had turned out so awfully, but the words stuck in my throat. I could only pray that he wouldn't take it out on Dux. He smiled, gave my shoulder a pat, and said he'd enjoyed the dinner, but I thought, I'd be willing to bet he'll go to a restaurant and have a square meal before he turns in.

When the door closed behind him, Dux threw himself into our easy chair and pulled me down onto his lap. "Baby, I'm sorry I laughed," he chuckled. "But you don't know how funny you looked sitting in the soup — madder than a wet hen! "

I tried to get up, but he held me close. Presently I stopped struggling and leaned against him. " I — I wanted you to be proud of m-me," I said miserably.

" I *am* proud, darling, very proud of you." His fingers touched my cheek in a caressing gesture. " And your cooking is improving too. That cake was delicious."

The cake, the *one* thing I had not made! I looked up at him and opened my mouth to tell him, then closed it firmly. There's bliss in ignorance, I decided, and snuggled closer. " I don't know what I'd do without you," I whispered. " You're a wonderful husband. You'll make a wonderful father."

Then I remembered and sat up straight on his lap. " I forgot to read Mother's letter," I said, reaching for it under the magazines on the table. " Want me to read it out loud? "

" M-mm," he murmured, kissing the back of my neck.

Suddenly I jumped. " Mother! " I squealed. " Oh, Dux! "

" What is it? " he asked quickly. " What's the matter? "

I gulped and gave him the letter. " Just read this. I can't believe it! *Mother's* going to have a baby too! "

7

Neither dux nor I wanted to live in the East, so when a doctor confirmed my suspicions that Mother wasn't the only pregnant woman in our family, we decided to go back to Kentucky. Dux wrote to a man he knew in Louisville, and when the answer came it said there was an opening for a draftsman in the engineering department of the Gas Company there. It didn't pay as much as we'd expected, but it was a start in the right direction. Dux got the job, borrowed the money to buy our railroad tickets, and we left New York for the Bluegrass State.

After spending a day with the folks in West Liberty, we went to Louisville and settled down in a couple of furnished rooms near the Gas Company office. Dux liked his job and enthusiastically got out his books and started to study at night. He also began working overtime, reaching out for new goals, eager to learn, through experience and observation, every facet of a business that had captured his imagination and beckoned to a rewarding future ahead.

I spent the days keeping house and trying to learn to knit tiny garments. They weren't needed, though, because Mother sewed, knitted, and crocheted two of everything — one in blue and one in pink. She was sure she'd have a boy and, for some obscure reason, thought we'd have a girl.

It was fun getting the packages from her, and I handled the little clothes so much that they had to be laundered three times before my baby came.

In October, Dad telephoned to say that Master Russell Acheson Baldwin had arrived, squalling his lungs out. Mother, he said, was doing as well as could be expected. I didn't like the sound of that, but he wouldn't say any more. Mother was still not well when our son was born six weeks later. Mrs. Addison, the wife of Dux's boss, went to the hospital with us and stayed until after it was all over.

Poor Dux looked as if he'd been drawn through a wringer. " Was it very bad, darling? " he asked when they let him come into my room.

" Not too bad — Isn't it wonderful? We've got a son! " I said sleepily. " Wait till you see him. He's beautiful." I couldn't stay awake. Reaching for Dux's hand, I closed my eyes.

When I opened them again, a beaming nurse was holding the baby up for Dux to see and his fuzzy little head wobbled. " Isn't him cunnin'? Isn't him the sweetest itty bitsy? " she cooed proudly, as if she had produced him herself.

Dux looked at his son, an anxious expression on his face. " Is — is he all right? "

" All right? " I cried indignantly. " Of course he's all right! He's a beautiful baby! "

" Yes, yes, dear, of course." He came over to the bed, leaned down, and kissed me. " It's just that I never saw a new one before and — "

" Don't you really think he's beautiful, Dux? " I felt the tears spill over on my cheeks.

" Sure, I think he's beautiful, darling." He slipped an arm under my shoulders and drew me to him. " Of course he's beautiful, and you're beautiful — and I've missed you so."

I wasn't quite convinced, but the nurse made him leave and took the baby back to the nursery. " Never mind," I told myself. " He can't help it if he doesn't feel like a mother. We're a family — Dux, our baby, and me — one for all and all for one." I touched my flat stomach with proud satisfaction and finally drifted off to sleep.

Howard Lawrence, Junior, was quite a name for such a little mite, so we started calling him " Buddy," and he was a source of never-ending joy to his doting parents. When he grew rosy and plump, Dux got over being afraid of him and often gave him his six o'clock bottle.

Buddy was a little past five months old when Dux came home one night looking like a little boy who'd just seen Santa Claus. I was feeding the baby, wondering what had happened at the office to make him so late, when he came in the door.

" Good news, isn't it? " I said, when he bent to kiss me. " It's written all over you."

" Sure is! " He threw his hat on the floor and sat down opposite me. " Last month when Addison sent me down to Scottsville to study those wells and write a report — remember? "

" Yes, I remember," I said, and waited.

" I wondered about it at the time. Now it seems it was a test to find out how much I know about geology," he went on. " And today Addison told me I've been selected to head a company that he, Mr. Lewis, and some bankers have formed to drill for oil."

" Oh," I whispered, " that's wonderful! " thinking, His oil field experience and his hours of study and work are beginning to pay off!

" They've even named it the ' Dux Oil Company,' " he said, a bit sheepishly, but I knew he was tickled pink. " They've put up enough money to buy a rig and drill four wells. My salary is to be increased twenty-five dollars —

and I'm also to have some stock." He sat down and propped his feet on a chair, and my thoughts raced ahead to all the things the extra money would buy. Up until then we'd never had a penny to spare.

"The rig and tools will be in sometime next week. I've got a secondhand Ford the Company bought, and I have to be in Tompkinsville early Monday morning." As he spoke, Dux's eyes brightened with anticipation. "Think you can be ready to leave in four days?"

"Oh, for goodness' sake, I could be ready in one day. All we have is Buddy's crib, our clothes, and the few wedding gifts we upacked from our things at Mother's." Then a thought struck me. "Why can't we drive to West Liberty for a day? I'm worried about Mother."

"That's O.K.," he agreed. "That is, if Addison says we can use the Company car."

Mr. Addison not only gave us permission to use the car, but told Dux to take Thursday and Friday off. We worked late into the night packing and cleaning the rooms we were leaving, and set out for West Liberty the following day.

We found Mother walking on crutches. Something like paralysis had set in after Russell's birth, and the doctors couldn't seem to find the trouble. She looked so wan and thin that it almost broke my heart, but she smiled cheerfully at neighbors and relatives coming in to see our babies, who were dressed exactly alike — one in pink and one in blue!

We left at dawn on Sunday morning. In plenty of time, we thought, to drive to Tompkinsville before dark that night — and it would have been if the roads hadn't been so muddy and if we hadn't had three flat tires! We didn't mind except for Buddy, and Buddy wouldn't have minded either if his milk hadn't soured. He was a good baby and took traveling or anything in his stride, just so he ate regularly. But he was screaming with rage when we finally pulled up in front of the hotel in Horse Cave, Kentucky. It was after ten o'clock, and all the restaurants we'd passed were closed. Dux carried the suitcases into the lobby and I followed with the baby, still yelling, his flailing arms knocking my hat over one eye.

The sleepy night clerk opened his eyes wide and stared at us, running his hand over his bald head. I jounced Buddy up and down, trying to quiet him and biting my lips to keep my own tears back, while Dux asked for milk and a room for the night.

"You can have a room," the old man drawled. "But the kitchen's locked this time o' night — and I ain't got no key."

I sank down in the nearest chair. "But what'll we do?" I demanded. "He's *hungry* and the milk is *sour!*"

"Oh, well now" — he took a key from a board hanging on the wall behind the desk and gave it to Dux — "you all go upstairs. I'll get some milk for the little feller."

About ten minutes later he knocked at the door and handed me a small pitcher of warm milk, and stood watching while I poured it into the bottle, put the nipple on, and thrust it into Buddy's angry mouth. With satisfied gurgles, the baby drew hungrily on the nipple, looking around at us with half-closed eyes in complete contentment.

Handing the pitcher back, I asked, "Where did you get the milk?"

He ran his hand over his bald head in the familiar gesture and said: "Well, pshaw, I just went out and milked somebody's cow. Don't know whose 'twas." He grinned at us, backed out the door, and closed it softly behind him.

We lived at the Newberry Hotel in Tompkinsville for a few days, and it wasn't too bad — at least, not until I

73

happened to lift the lid of the keg they kept the sorghum in. I loved hot biscuits and sorghum molasses. But when I saw the multitude of flies that had died trying to get out of the thick, sticky goodness, I lost my appetite completely.

Dux was drilling a well on the Dean lease, about five miles out of town, and he persuaded Mrs. Dean to let us have room and board. Their farmhouse was small, but she gave us the " parlor." It was the front room, crowded with a brass bed, plump with feather ticking and covered with an openwork crocheted counterpane over blue sateen; an old-fashioned organ; and a red-plush sofa in front of the lace-curtained window. Large gold-framed pictures of long-dead relatives hung on the walls, and a velvety album of tintypes lay beside the flowered china lamp on the blue-fringed cloth of the small table. We set up the baby's crib in front of the organ.

Mrs. Dean was a good cook, and on sunny days we thoroughly enjoyed her meals, served outside under the huge shady elm. But on rainy days it was different. Her aged mother lived in the kitchen, spending most of her days in bed, behind a patchwork quilt hung from the ceiling. With no dining room, we ate in the kitchen on the bad days, but the patchwork quilt didn't keep us from hearing the old lady's hawking noises when she tried to clear her throat. Nor did it keep us from hearing the rattle of the lid to the slop jar that she kept beside her bed.

And I never did get used to the flies. With no screens, they were abundant. During meals, Mrs. Dean and her husband, Benny, took turns wielding the old-fashioned fan, made from hanging newspaper strips pasted on a broom handle.

Most of the spring days I spent down by the rig, spreading a blanket for Buddy, watching the walking beam move up and down, up and down, and listening to the clang-

clang of the jars in the hole. Buddy played or napped, and I read or dreamed of things to come — building town houses, summer cottages, picking out fancy schools for all my children. I even went cruising on a luxurious yacht — quite a feat to picture, since I had never seen a yacht of any kind.

But Dux loved boats and I knew that if he ever did make money, he'd want a boat, at least a small one. He never tired of talking about the sailboat he'd bought for a song and rebuilt in the years before I met him, the one he got his nickname from, or of the months he'd worked for a man who owned a pleasure craft on Sheepshead Bay.

One afternoon I was sitting on the blanket playing with Buddy when Mrs. Dean joined us. " Would you mind driving me into town? " she asked. " I've saved up enough egg money for some goods. I want to try to make me a new dress."

" I'd love to," I said, " if Dux will let me drive the Company car." She really needs a new dress, I thought. All I'd ever seen her wear was dingy black cotton, with faded aprons made from feed sacks. Picking Buddy up, I walked over to the rig to ask Dux about using the car.

" You know I don't like it — but it just so happens that we need new belting for the blowers, so you go ahead." He took a pencil stub from his shirt pocket, tore a piece of paper from his notebook, and wrote on it. " Here, give this to Don at the supply store; he'll put the belting in the car."

All the way into town I kept thinking how I'd like to fix Mrs. Dean up: change the way she wore her hair, get some color on her face, put her in a bright-colored dress that had some line to it. She'd really be a pretty woman. I smiled to myself, thinking of how Benny's face would look if he saw his wife prettied up. Benny was a good sort when he stopped drinking moonshine — which wasn't often. But at times when he was sober he'd bring her horehound candy, slap her on her backside, and say, " Best darn woman in Monroe County! " Her face would flush with pleasure, but she'd look at us in embarrassment and say to him, " Go 'long with you — you old fool! "

We stopped in front of the dry-goods store and got out of the car. " Don't let me forget that stuff for Dux," I said, taking Buddy from her arms. Inside the store I stopped in front of bright-colored calico and gingham bolts stacked on the counter. " Oh, Mrs. Dean, look at that lovely candy-stripe! "

" Yes, it's pretty," she said, and went on toward the bolts of black goods stacked on another counter.

" You aren't going to get *black* again? "

Startled, she turned to me. " Why, what else would I get? "

" Something pretty, like this." I sat Buddy on the counter, holding his wiggling little body with one arm, and lifted a corner of the striped calico. " Or this," I added, touching a finger to a red-and-white polka dot.

The clerk deftly jerked the two bolts from the stack. Mrs. Dean looked at them longingly but shook her head. " Oh, not for *me!* " she said. " My goodness, I'm forty years old! "

Forty didn't seem old to me — not after Mother had a baby at thirty-six — so I kept egging her on to get something besides black. We finally settled on gray gingham with tiny pink flowers — not as bright and colorful as the other goods, but pretty.

We argued again over a pattern, but I picked out one with ruffles from the *Delineator*, promising to help her make the dress — sheer bluff on my part, because I didn't know anything about sewing. It was one of the things Mother used to say she should teach me, but somehow she never got around to doing it. At school, in domestic science, we never went beyond making different kinds of stitches in a piece of cloth.

We stopped at the rig with the stuff for Dux and drove on up to the house. It was still early, so I tied Buddy in a chair, spread the goods out on our bed, pinned the pattern in place, and carefully cut it out. Mrs. Dean rolled her sewing machine into our room, for I'd talked her into surprising Benny.

During the next three days we sewed — and ripped! But at last the dress was finished, and it *did* fit, even though we had to take a seam in here and let one out there. In fact, it was such a good fit that Mrs. Dean was a little apprehensive — said it showed her shape too much — but I just laughed at her. She washed her hair and I persuaded her to let me wave the front with the curling irons and fix it on top of her head instead of the usual knot at the back. While she got supper I pressed the dress and she was all ready when the men came in.

Benny stood in the doorway and gaped at her. " Ma! " His voice cracked. " W-why, Ma! " It seemed to me that he tried to stand straighter, tried to lift his stooped shoulders. She blushed from so much attention, and we glimpsed the beauty that must have been hers back in the days when they fell in love.

Later, when Dux and I were getting ready for bed, he said, " I didn't know you could sew, Shortie."

" Can't really. I only helped, and the pattern wasn't hard to follow. She did look nice, didn't she? "

" Very nice. You did a good job." He looked at me thoughtfully. " How about making me a pair of engineering breeches? "

" You're fooling! " I laughed. " But I am going to get some goods and make Buddy and Russell each a pair of rompers. Mrs. Dean said I could use her sewing machine."

The next week I started on the rompers and finally got them finished. Mrs. Dean worked the buttonholes for me. I felt a surge of pride when I wrapped Russell's pair up on Friday and mailed the package off to Mother.

On Saturday afternoon Buddy and I drove into town with Dux and waited in the car while he went to the stores to buy things for the job. As we started back, he dropped a brown bundle beside me on the seat.

" What's that? " I asked, thinking it didn't look like anything to be used on a drilling rig.

" Khaki," he said, looking straight ahead at the road.

" Khaki? " I looked at him suspiciously.

He turned to me briefly and smiled. " For you, honey. To make me a pair of breeches."

" Oh, no, Dux! I *can't!* " The very thought made me shudder. " You *know* I can't sew! "

" You made those rompers," he pointed out. " You helped make Mrs. Dean's dress." He patted my knee. " My girl can do anything she makes up her mind to."

" That's the way you always get me to do things you know I shouldn't have to do," I said crossly. " What's wrong with the ones you buy? "

" They don't fit in the waist, honey — and they don't snug my hips." He sighed. " But never mind, if you don't want to do it."

For the rest of the way we rode in silence. I knew how fussy Dux was about his engineering clothes. He didn't seem to care what the other kind looked like, even paid more for his work things. But if the stores couldn't fit his slender hips, how in the world did he expect *me* to?

When we got back, he carried Buddy and the bundle to our room, tossed the khaki on the bed, and said: " Get his bottle. I'll feed him and put him to bed for you."

After supper, he got out an old pair of engineering pants

78

made by a tailor, ripped them up for a pattern, and started to pin a piece to the khaki spread out on the bed. I stood it as long as I could.

"Oh, get away," I said, pushing against him. "I'll do it."

He grinned and gave me a quick hug. "I thought you would, honey. I'll bet you do a swell job too."

The following week I began to work on the breeches. I sewed by day and ripped by night. Buddy and I both suffered and wept together in frustration. He was trying to cut a tooth and I was trying to be as clever as my husband thought I was. Once, losing my temper completely, I threw those pants clear across the room, ready to quit, but when I thought of the preposterous faith in Dux's hazel eyes, I picked them up again.

At last my aching fingers held up the finished breeches, complete to the tiny watch pocket that sagged a trifle. I could hardly believe I'd really done it! I showed them to Mrs. Dean, and she was as proud of the accomplishment as I.

"Let me nurse the baby while you get them pressed," she said. "Won't your man be surprised?"

Dux had been so busy for several months that I hadn't seen much of him — just at mealtime and late at nights. Three wells had been put down, only to result in dry holes, and the Company funds were beginning to run low. Dux had tried to hide his disappointment, but I could hear discouragement in the tone of his voice. They were now on the fourth well, and I knew he was worried. He'd said they were almost to the top of the formation and, so far, no sign of oil. This, I knew, was the last chance. If this well came in another duster, the Dux Oil Company was finished. My mouth went dry when I thought of what failure would mean to Dux.

When he came home for supper that night and saw the

pants laid out on the bed, he stood silent for a long moment. Then he hugged me and he was laughing. " You did it, darling! " His eyes were bright as he kissed me. " But I knew all the time you could."

A few days later I was sitting in the shade of the big oak down by the rig, trying to keep my wiggling son on the blanket, when Dux came over and stretched out alongside the baby.

" About time you got a little rest," I scolded, noting his tired eyes, the new lines in his face. " Dux, you know Mr. Addison and Mr. Lewis don't expect you to work night and day."

" Only way I can learn, Shortie — watch every movement of the guy who knows," he said, poking a finger at Buddy's tummy to make him laugh. " If this well is a dud, I can do contract work, do the actual drilling myself."

" But why would *you* have to do it? "

" Because drillers cost money and they're hard to get." He sat up and lighted a cigarette. " And it's the only way the Company can keep going."

" Well, I've got a hunch you'll strike it this time," I said, hoping my words would prove prophetic.

" We'll know pretty soon now." He brushed imaginary dirt from the leg of his new breeches, took off his cap, and ran a hand over his hair which should have been trimmed a week ago, and put it on again.

" Will it be today or — " I began.

" Listen! " He jumped up and stood still. The clang of the drilling bits sounded the same to me. " Something's in the hole," he cried, and ran toward the well just as the driller yelled,

" Somethin's in the hole! "

Scarcely breathing, I watched the men start to pull the tools from the hole. Dux leaned down, placed his hand close to the wire line that was slowly bringing up the drilling bit, then straightened and grinned at the chunky driller and the snub-nosed tool-dresser. I thought of the last three times they'd reached the top of the formation in the other wells — the excitement, the buoyant expectancy they'd felt — and my throat tightened as I remembered Dux's face when the holes filled up with salt water. If only . . .

Dux turned and motioned to me. Forgetting Buddy, I ran toward the rig and stopped just short of the derrick floor. " Is it, Dux? " I cried above the noisy clash of the bull wheel's gears, the bark of the engine. " Oh, is it? "

" I think so," he shouted. " I can smell gas! "

Unable to move, I stared at the stem coming out of the hole — the drilling bit — then I let out a wild cry. Slimy, darkish liquid dripped from the tools — rich, beautiful, golden-brown oil!

My knees buckled and I slid to the ground, oblivious of the mud, my heart filled to the brim. The men threw their caps into the air with childish glee. Dux jumped off the derrick floor, swung me around, and leaped back. Then the driller hooked the dripping tools to one side, lowered the bailer into the hole, and started slowly to pull it up.

All at once, a spray of rich, gushing oil shot up over the mast, breaking into golden-brown rain that drenched us all. Too fascinated to get out of the way, I felt the wonderful goo on my face, felt it coming down my arms. Suddenly, I thought of my baby and ran back to him. He had wiggled off the blanket and was calmly stuffing sod into his mouth, unmindful of the breathless excitement around him. I snatched him up and ran to the house to tell Mrs. Dean the good news.

Later, after they'd capped the flow — shut the well in — Dux sent me into Tompkinsville to call Mr. Addison. " Tell him the well flowed from a depth of three hundred and ten feet," he said, and his eyes shone. " That'll get 'em down here in a hurry! " He also gave me a list of stuff needed for tubing the well.

I drove along the country road singing at the top of my lungs, stopping in the middle of a note to giggle foolishly. My young son laughed too and looked at me as if he thought his mother had suddenly gone crazy, as indeed she almost had — the happiest kind of crazy!

8

As DUX PUT IT, " All hell broke loose! " within the hour. There is no news that travels as fast as that of a wildcat strike, and this was the first oil well to be brought in in Monroe County.

A flood of excitement filled the countryside. People crowded into the lane, the pasture lot, and even the yard, until the Deans' property looked as if a huge tractor had plowed through it. Benny, effusively pompous and slightly drunk, let down the bars across the field entrance, inviting them all in.

Oil scouts, " leasehounds," promoters, came from everywhere. Businessmen from surrounding towns and villages closed up shop and spent hours on the site. Farmers came from miles around, arriving on horseback, in wagons, buckboards, and trucks. They leaned against vehicles or squatted on the ground, some chewing tobacco, others blades of grass. Some whittled, others idly flipped pocketknives into the ground — all of them in high good humor, swapping stories and talking of the oil boom. A holiday atmosphere prevailed and it was like a carnival or county fair.

Mr. Addison and Mr. Lewis brought the Dux Company stockholders from Louisville and, besides having to park their car down on the highway, they had to elbow their way to the rig. An expression of odd disbelief was on Mr. Addison's face as he said,

"This is something I've read about, but never thought I'd see."

They put up at the crowded Newberry Hotel and didn't leave until after the well was tubed, spending every waking hour near the rig. Mrs. Dean let me fix picnic lunches and, after the tanks were set, the well was opened and I stood with Dux and the men and stared at the pure, rich crude oil pushing its way up through the casing as the tubing was lowered — an intermittent spray of magic!

But Dux didn't seem as happy about the well as I'd expected him to be and, when I casually remarked that it was going to be fun to shop and ignore the price tags, he shook his head.

"Don't you go spending till you've got the money in your pocket," he warned.

"But an oil well — isn't that money in my pocket?" I asked in surprise.

"Could be — but you wait. This oil could be in a pocket too." He grinned at his pun, then said seriously, "If it is — well, we'll be lucky to get our expenses."

Later, a man came up from Texas and made Dux an offer to buy the well and leases. "I'm not sure it's worth the price you're offering; the geology in this part of the country — " Dux started to tell him.

"I know all that," the man said impatiently. "But we're prepared to gamble. Get in touch with your company as soon as possible and let me know."

Dux tried his best to get them to sell and Mr. Addison agreed with him. But Mr. Lewis and the others wouldn't hear of it. The following week, the rig was moved to the next location and the first offset well spudded in.

After the oil well stopped flowing, it was put on the pump, and production began gradually to decline. By the first of October Dux said it didn't even pay to keep the pump going. It was all over; our bubble had burst and my pocket was empty!

"Well, you can't miss what you haven't had," Dux said philosophically.

Poor Benny Dean couldn't take it. Success had gone to his head and he drank for joy. Now that it was leaving him, he felt sorry for himself and drank more and more — to drown his troubles, he said. We felt very sorry for Mrs. Dean, and she begged Dux to do something.

"I've been talking to him," Dux told her. "But you can't reason with moonshine."

One day he went into town and didn't come home all night. The next morning his loyal wife said tearfully: "Please go after him, Mr. Gentry. He's either hurt or in jail. I know he's a triflin' good-for-nothin', but he's mine! "

Dux drove into town early the next morning and, sure enough, found Benny in jail, cut and bruised from getting the worst of a fight. After he had paid his bail and they started for home, Dux lectured him all the way. Benny got very penitent, vowing by everything holy that he'd let the powerful stuff alone. And, for a time, he did. But when both the first and second offset wells came in dry holes, he forgot all about his promises and went back to his little brown jug.

At last the rig was moved off the Deans' property and Dux, upon orders from the Oil Company, began doing contract work for people — mostly doctors and lawyers who had bought leases and farms, positive that all they had to do to get rich was to get a well down. Drilling masts sprang up everywhere and dry holes flourished, with here and there a small showing of gas or oil. But hope dies hard and Dux had enough work to keep him busy all winter and to keep the treasurer of the Dux Oil Company happy.

After the first contract job, he got along all right. But on the first well he ever drilled all by himself, he " sweated blood," as he expressed it. Sort of like my first sewing! He drilled a while, got a crooked hole, and spent hours undoing his work. Drilled a while more, lost the tools, and spent hours on a fishing job. For weeks, he worked darn near all day and all night, and I began to worry.

He lost weight and there was a kind of feverish alertness, a wariness, in his eyes that I'd never seen before. But he kept on doggedly, and finally his capable hands on the wire line could feel what was happening in the dark below, could feel down the muddy pipe to guide the drilling bit.

About that time Mrs. Dean's old mother passed on. We all missed her, but there was no denying that our meals were much more pleasant. Mrs. Dean took advantage of the Indian summer days to serve meals outdoors, picnic-fashion, while the kitchen got a new coat of yellow paint and we hung the blue-checked curtains I'd made.

During the long days of winter she often let me cook, and I learned to make biscuits, cakes, and other good things, even to Dux's favorite chess pie. And on Buddy's birthday, I took a particular delight in baking a fancy cake. The old wood range and I became quite friendly, and I longed more than ever for a kitchen of my own. But it wasn't any use; there were simply no housekeeping rooms to be had.

Sometime in January, Dux brought in a well with a fair showing of oil, but not enough for commercial purposes. He decided to shoot it to increase the flow if possible, and we drove into Tompkinsville for dynamite, leaving Buddy with Mrs. Dean. Dux loaded the stuff in the back of the Ford and I held the box of caps in my lap as we bumped along the frozen, rutty road back home. Grandma used to say the Lord takes care of children and fools — I've often wondered what category He put us under.

The next morning Mrs. Dean and some of her friends drove over to the well with me. Dux told us where to park the car — close enough to see, yet far enough away to be out of range of falling rock. It was terribly exciting and I felt a surge of pride in my husband.

We watched the men tie sticks of dynamite all around a piece of wood, a couple of inches thick and about sixteen feet long, then lower it into the hole with some sort of hook on the end of the bailer.

" How're they goin' to get it lit? " one of the women asked.

" With a jack-squib," I answered. " That's a stick of dynamite with a percussion cap inside and a long fuse attached to it."

" Oh! " She looked at me queerly.

" Well, my goodness — " I smiled at her awed expression, " you can't live around oil and gas fields as I have without absorbing *some* knowledge. And Dux is awfully good about answering my dumb questions."

" Look," Mrs. Dean cried, " they're lightin' the fuse."

Dux dropped the lighted jack-squib into the hole, and joined the men out in the field.

We got out of the car and stood waiting. There was a slight thud, like the muffled sound of a shot. Then came a rumble like faraway thunder, which grew louder until it reached a mighty roar as the water and sand and rocks shot up the pipe with the impact of a thousand bullets, and rained debris for rods around the well. It was over quickly and the men ran back to see if it had done any good.

It hadn't. There wasn't enough oil to bother with, so they pulled the pipe, plugged the hole, and abandoned the well.

~

Spring weather came early that year. Mrs. Dean and I spent hours planting petunias in the window boxes, nasturtiums along the fence, and pinks in her perennial bed. I found an old cracked chamber pot with a broken handle out by the woodshed and potted a begonia Mrs. Dean let me have. Somehow it sort of gave our room a touch of home.

One Saturday evening in March, Dux and I were driving into Tompkinsville for supplies and he seemed a little more quiet than usual.

" Worrying about something, honey? " I asked.

" No — just thinking," he said. " This isn't much of a life for a girl. How'd you like to have a place of your own, Shortie? "

" Oh, golly! " I glanced at him and laughed shortly. " Don't tempt me." I knew that I'd go with him to the ends of the earth no matter how I had to live.

" Well, there's plenty of work in this area," he went on. " I know where I can pick up a tent or two. I'll see what I can do."

What he did was most ingenious. In the field below the Deans' house, he built a rough wooden platform. Then he set up three small tents and put a roof over the space where they came together, screening it in. He also put screening all around the sides, so that in hot weather all we had to do was to roll the tents up to the top of the screening. We ate in the space that was roofed. One tent was the living room, one our bedroom, and the other the kitchen.

I even had hot water — that is, I did when the sun shone! Dux put two barrels up on a rack, ran a pipe from them into my kitchen, and put a spigot on the end. Water was pumped into the barrels from an old cistern on the property, but we had to carry our drinking water from the Deans' well.

Then he built a tiny porch with a railing around it and a miniature gate — a perfect playpen for Buddy when the gate was hooked.

We didn't have much to spend, but we bought a bed, a larger crib for the baby, some dishes, pots and pans, a coal-oil stove to cook with, and put linoleum on the floors. From a secondhand store in Tompkinsville I bought discarded pieces of furniture — an old rocker, some straight chairs, a small table, and two chests of drawers. Mrs. Dean helped me paint them and gave me a pair of bed pillows.

"Of course," Dux said on the day we moved in, "it's not the same as a house, but it'll give us more privacy and it's *ours* — " He broke off then and we looked at each other. I felt my lips tremble and he said gently:

"Did you think I didn't know how you felt? Did you think I didn't want a place of our own too?"

Someday we'll have a real house, I thought, but it can't possibly mean to us what this one does — our *first*. I looked from the tents to Dux and couldn't hold back any longer. Putting my head on his shoulder, I began to cry.

Mother and Dad wrote that they were anxious to see our wonderful canvas home and planned to come for a visit as soon as Mother was able. She still walked on crutches, was still under the care of a doctor. They sent us a lot of jellies, home-canned fruit, and a ham. My mouth watered as I pulled it out of the gunny sack and pushed the old newspapers from around it. We liked nothing better than hickory-smoked country ham. I cut a slice, then cried out in disgust, "Skippers!" Tiny, wiggling little old white worms!

"Got something good from your pa?" I turned to see Mrs. Dean opening the screen door, pushing her sunbonnet back on her head with hands that were rough and red from scrubbing.

89

"I thought so. It's a ham — but it's got skippers in it."
I made a face and started to wrap it up to throw away.

"Here — let's see." She peered at the place where I'd
cut the slice. "Why, child, there ain't nary a thing wrong
with that — it's plumb good. Just wash them skippers
out."

I looked at her in astonishment. "I wouldn't eat that
meat for *anything!*" I exclaimed. "Dad'll hate to hear
about it. He buys his hams from a farmer over on Grassy
Creek, and they're usually good."

"Well, Land o' Goshen," she said, wrapping the newspapers around it, "a few little ole skippers won't hurt it
none. I'll take it if you don't want it."

"Why, of course you can have it, but you mean you'd
eat it?" I asked, unable to believe my ears.

She nodded. "As hard up as we are, it'll come in purty
handy." She thrust it back into the gunny sack, tucked it
under her arm, and smiled. "Much obliged," she said as she
went out the door.

After supper that night, I put Buddy to bed and went
out on the porch where Dux sat reading. I told him about
the ham.

"Well," he said. "I don't suppose it'll kill them to eat
it, but I wouldn't want — " He broke off suddenly and
jumped to his feet. "Look at that sky — looks like a fire!"

The sky grew a deeper pink as we watched.

"Must be the Railey well — I heard they'd struck gas,"
Dux said as he grabbed his hat. He leaped over the porch
railing toward the car and was gone before I could make a
protest.

A feeling of panic washed over me as I watched the sky
get brighter and brighter, glimpsed the red flames as they
shot upward and then fell back. Fires have always been the
greatest fear of the well drillers, most of them dangerous

to put out, and I worried. I knew that Dux, with his daring and his insatiate desire for actual experience in every phase of his chosen career, would walk right into it. I had even heard him discuss ways and means of putting out such fires.

The Deans had gone to Glasgow with relatives, so there was no one to talk to, nothing to do until Dux came home. I didn't go to bed because I knew I couldn't sleep. Anyway, Buddy kept waking up and crying — another tooth, I thought, as I cuddled his warm little body in the rocking chair.

At dawn, I heard a car and ran to the door. It was Dux and he looked worn out, his face streaming with perspiration, his clothes grimy, and he smelled of singeing.

" It's out," he grinned, mopping his face. " And I'm hungry."

He sat at the table and, while I fried bacon and scrambled eggs, he talked tiredly. " They really needed help. By the time I got there, they'd taken the driller and tool-dresser in to the Glasgow hospital."

" Were they badly burned? "

" Don't think so. It wasn't a big fire. They must have hit a pocket of gas and it ignited from sparks of the gasoline engine."

" How'd you put it out? " I set the bacon and eggs in front of him and poured a cup of coffee.

" Well, we sent a man in for dynamite; then we got several mule teams and pulled what was left of the rig out of the way." He ate hungrily for a minute and went on, " We propped some corrugated sheeting up to keep the heat off while we drove two pieces of bent pipe into the ground, wired the dynamite, and ran the wire to a spark plug in my car."

" Wasn't that dangerous? "

He shook his head. " No — I got everybody out of the way, set off the shot, and poof — " he flipped his fingers, " that's all there was to it."

" You don't fool me, talking as if it's nothing," I said. " You're in danger all the time when you're drilling."

" Oh, no, baby. There's no danger if you know what you're doing," he said. " Of course you've got to look ahead and take precautions. But most of the fires, tools blowing out of the hole, things like that, are caused by carelessness."

Long after he went to sleep, I lay awake thinking of the tomorrows, of the things that could happen — the unexpected things you couldn't be prepared for. I'd never realized before the hazards in the life of an oil and gas engineer; it was like living in the shadow of a volcano! I moved closer to Dux and remembered Miss Abby's words: " Never borrow trouble. Keep looking ahead, have faith in God and the one you love — the future will take care of itself."

9

THE NEXT DAY Buddy was so cross that I couldn't do a thing but sit and rock him. Dux and Benny had brought Mrs. Dean's sewing machine down for me to use and I was in the throes of another pair of breeches — this time, black corduroy — but every time I tried to put Buddy down, he grabbed me around the neck and screamed. Then he'd snuggle in my arms contentedly, look up at me with an angelic smile, and chuckle in a way that made me wonder if I were being duped.

A little before noon Mrs. Dean came down — said she heard Buddy screaming and wondered what the trouble was.

" I don't know what's the matter with him," I said wearily. "He won't eat — threw his bottle down and broke it and dumped his oatmeal on the floor! "

" He don't look so peart — but then most young'uns get puny, times they're cuttin' teeth." She held her arms out to him, but he dug his head into my shoulder, yelling, " No . . . no . . . no! "

" Why, precious — this is Mrs. Dean," I said. " You've always loved her." But he only clung the harder to me. " Maybe we should take him in to Louisville to Dr. Fulton. He hasn't had a checkup in six months."

" Best do that — or else give him sulphur an' molasses. That's good for a body, come spring. I've been noticin' him pickin' at his little nose too, and that's a sure sign of worms." Mrs. Dean got up, patted Buddy on his curly head, and turned toward the door. " I better be gettin' back; time to cook dinner for Benny. If I can help you, call."

Dux and I talked it over that night and decided to take Buddy to Louisville. " Addison wants me in the office for a few days anyway, so you get to the telephone in the morning and call Dr. Fulton for an appointment."

He kept the baby while I drove to the country store, down the road a piece, to use the telephone. The nurse said Dr. Fulton was out of the city but would be back on the following Friday. She would make the appointment for us and, upon my arrival in Louisville, I was to phone her to find out the hour.

We were almost ready to leave on Thursday when a man came to our tents to talk about contracting for a well. I waited impatiently in the bedroom until he left.

" I can't leave until Saturday now, honey," Dux said. " But there's a train that leaves Glasgow Junction around eight in the morning that'll get you there by noon."

" But I've never gone any place without you — " I began.

" You'll be all right. Take a taxi and go to the Addisons' as soon as you get in. Mrs. Addison will probably go with you to see Dr. Fulton," he said. " And don't let me forget to give you my reports. I should have sent them to Addison last week."

The next morning Dux drove us to Glasgow Junction and put us on the train, pushing my small bag and the baby's folded sulky under the seat. " I'll be at the Newberry Hotel to meet a man around four this afternoon," he told me. " We'll eat supper there, so you telephone me, let me know what the doctor says, and I'll be able to tell you when I'll get in."

He kissed me good-by just as the brakeman called, "All aboard." "You be careful," he yelled, and hopped off the moving train. I nodded and waved till he dwindled from view.

I took off Buddy's coat and cap, gave him a graham cracker, and opened the new magazine Dux had bought in the drugstore. The conductor came by and ran his big hand over the baby's blond curls and Buddy, now in the best of spirits, grinned up at him. It occurred to me that I might just as well have postponed the visit to the doctor and waited until Dux could come with us. However, there was no turning back now.

"Going down to the Derby?" the conductor asked as he punched my ticket.

Startled, I shook my head. I'd forgotten that this was the first Friday in May and tomorrow would be Derby Day. I knew I couldn't go barging in on the Addisons, even though they had invited me to come at any time. They always had a house full of guests during the races. A baby — even a good baby like Buddy — would only add to the confusion. So I thought, I'll phone the doctor to check on the appointment, then get a room at the Seelbach and call Dux.

At Louisville, I took a cab to the Gas Company offices to deliver Dux's reports. The driver, with the usual courtesy of Louisville taximen, helped me to unfold the baby's sulky and even took time to tie my small suitcase to the back so that it wouldn't slip. In the engineering department I was made welcome by the people I knew, and the girls took Buddy and played with him, getting him to pat-a-cake and throw kisses — he loved showing off — while I used the telephone.

I called the doctor's office, only to be told that he was still out of the city and would not return until Monday. But I wasn't too worried because Buddy was definitely better and the checkup could easily wait a few days.

When I phoned the Seelbach Hotel, the clerk queried, " Are you alone? " I didn't understand why that mattered, but I said yes. " No room," he snapped. I called three other hotels and got the same answer. I didn't mention my baby, because I'd learned before when we were trying to find furnished rooms that most people didn't want babies as guests. It didn't occur to me that there might be some prejudice against women arriving alone during Derby Week, though I did feel that the hotel clerks had been unnecessarily abrupt.

But I wasn't worried about that either, and when I went downstairs I asked the elevator girl if she knew of any rooming houses.

" There used to be some over on Fourth Street." She held the door and cooed at Buddy while I strapped him in the sulky.

Confidently, I walked toward Fourth Street and the warm spring air flowed through me. I loved being back in the city, loved wheeling my baby on a sidewalk. Country air might be pure, but you can't wheel a baby buggy on bumpy fields or dirt roads. This was a part of town I didn't know much about. But it must have been the pride of Louisville in the early days, I decided, noting the venerable shade trees and the spacious stone and brick houses set back from the street. Most of the lawns were unkempt now and the houses grimy from smoke and neglect.

At one place I noticed a group of girls out on the front lawn of a brownstone house and they seemed to be having fun. I opened the rusty gate and a buxom woman with carrot-red hair and tired-looking eyes jumped up and came toward me. She stood with her arms folded as if she would bar the way.

" What do you want, girlie? " she asked.

" I thought maybe you might have a room to rent? " I said, and heard the girls giggle.

She shook her head. " Afraid you've come to the wrong place, honey. I don't usually take roomers. This ain't a rooming house."

" Do you know of any? " I asked as I stooped to move Buddy, who had fallen asleep.

" No — can't say I do," she said, and I started out the gate. " Wait," she called after me as I clicked the latch. " Are you and your baby really stranded in town? "

I nodded, still hoping I wouldn't have to bother the Addisons.

She smiled. She wasn't at all bad-looking when she smiled, in spite of her two chins, her bulk, and her amazing red hair — probably as pretty as her daughters in her younger days.

" You come in, honey." She opened the gate wide, regarding me with sympathetic eyes. " I reckon I can take care of you — but ain't you got a husband? "

" Of course." I followed her up the walk. " He'll be here in a day or so. I couldn't get a hotel room — probably because of the races."

" Sure. And that husband of yours — he's got no business lettin' you run around alone when the races are on," she grumbled.

The girls smiled as we passed. They made a pretty picture sitting on the green grass with their colorful dresses, their rosy complexions and curly hair. They all looked about the same age, and I thought it was no wonder the woman had let herself go: she'd had her babies too fast, if all those six belonged to her.

We went inside the dark, musty hall and I lifted my sleeping son and pushed the sulky into a corner. The woman led the way up the bare steps. At the top of the stairs she jerked open a door that stuck.

"You'll be all right here — I'll get Joe to fix that door." She raised the shades. "Now, honey, don't you worry none. I'll be right next door."

I smiled. What did she think I was afraid of, for Pete's sake? I laid Buddy on the big bed and covered him, saying, "I'll go get my suitcase."

"No, let Joe get it." She went into the hall and shouted: "Joe! Hey Joe — get the lead out of your feet and come here!"

In a moment a door opened and a skinny, bald-headed little man came out, yawning and pulling a pair of red suspenders over his thin shoulders. "Whaddya want?" he said crossly. "Can't a guy get no sleep around here?"

"I want you should fix this here door and fetch this child's suitcase from downstairs," the woman told him.

"Huh?" His red eyes fell on me in sudden surprise and his head jerked back. Then he opened his mouth, but before he could speak, she gave him a push.

"Shut up! Go get that valise like I said."

"Sure, sure," he said and turned toward the stairs, still staring at me over his bony shoulder.

"Now, honey," the woman smiled again, "bathroom's across the hall, but you've got a washbowl and slop jar, so you don't need to leave your room. And don't forget — I'm takin' care of you." With that she went downstairs.

These were funny people, I thought, but then they meant well and I was grateful. I closed the door as far as it would go and unpacked the baby's things and my extra blouse. It was a relief not to have to worry about diapers for my sixteen-months-old son. Buddy didn't talk much, just jabbered, but we both understood his " Wee-wee."

At five o'clock Buddy and I went out to get some supper. When we came downstairs I glimpsed the girls in the parlor and hoped they would be there when I got back. I was hungry for young companionship and it was lonesome without Dux. Suddenly I remembered that he'd expected me to call him at the Newberry Hotel around four. He'd be frantic by this time.

We found a small restaurant and followed the waitress as she pushed her way to a table against the wall. Every place would be crowded until after the Derby. She lifted Buddy to the high chair and said, " He's a mighty pretty little boy," and pushed the chair against the table.

Buddy grabbed a spoon and started banging gleefully on the table. I tied a napkin around his chubby chin, took the spoon away, and gave him a cracker. The room was stuffy and hot and the clatter of dishes and metal trays rose above the voices of the customers. My eyes fell on the fly-specked clock on the wall and I looked around for the telephone, finding it on the wall back of our table.

I fixed Buddy's mashed potatoes and peas, poured his milk, and buttered a biscuit, then went to the telephone. In a few minutes Dux was on the wire and he began to fire a volley of questions at me.

" Where the heck have you been? Where are you? Why didn't you call me earlier, like you said? I've been trying to call the Addisons to make sure you were all right! "

" I'm sorry, honey. I was so busy looking for a place to stay and — "

" A place to stay? " he interrupted. " Where the devil are you? "

" I've got a room on Fourth Street," I said, and gave him the number. " I didn't want to stay at the Addisons' during the races; they always have a houseful. We forgot all about tomorrow being Derby Day."

" Darn it, Shortie, I wish you'd do what I tell you. Are you sure that place is O.K.? "

" Certainly, it's O.K.," I said stiffly, piqued by his attitude. " It's a family — a mother with several daughters. Nice people," I added, going overboard in a stubborn attempt to hold my ground. " You know — friendly and kind."

" Are you sure you're all right? "

" Of course I'm all right. After all, I'm a married woman and a mother — "

" Yeah, but . . ." He didn't sound very convinced. " Have you seen the doctor? " he said.

" Not yet," I answered. " He isn't back yet, but Buddy is feeling fine."

" O.K.," Dux said. " I'll be in around five thirty tomorrow."

I hung up the receiver, feeling resentful because I hated being treated like a child, and went back to our table where my dinner was beginning to get cold. I ate it, though, cleaned Buddy up, and went back to our room.

The house was quiet and I didn't see anybody. I put Buddy to bed, washed out my stockings and underthings, and finally crawled in beside him, after placing a chair under the knob of the swollen door that Joe never did fix. I must have fallen asleep, for suddenly I found myself sitting upright in bed. There were sounds of laughter coming from downstairs, and somewhere a phonograph was playing " Darktown Strutters' Ball." I thought: They're having a party. I wish they'd invited me.

For a long time I lay awake, wondering where Dux's next job would be and wondering where we'd live. Some new field, probably, and we'd pitch our tents on the edge of the lease. But someday we'd have a real home. Someday we'd have our own business. Of course it would have to be oil and gas — Dux wouldn't be happy with any other — but then he could hire men to stay out on the jobs and we'd live in a city or town near good schools and dig our roots in the ground. It would be fun to have neighbors and chat over the back fence; to have a yard full of flowers that I could pick for the table. It would be good to get away from the everlasting plunk-plunk of the drilling rigs, and never have to smell the pungent odor of crude oil — the stuff that always reminded me of sorghum molasses, but smelled terrible.

Buddy woke me early and I got us ready to go out for breakfast. No one seemed to be up, so I walked down the creaky stairs on tiptoe, sniffing stale cigar smoke, and peeked into the parlor. They must have had quite a party, judging from the cluttered room.

The sun was shining and the air smelled good. The streets were gay with flags and bunting. Men stood on corners with racing forms in their hands, talking and ges-ticulating, and newsboys shouted the morning track news. After breakfast we sat in the park for a long time, fed the pigeons, and watched the people on the street. I guess there is nothing more colorful than a Derby crowd, and the good weather had brought out a bumper crop that year.

On our way back to the room, I stopped at a Piggly Wiggly and bought lunch stuff and milk for Buddy, so I wouldn't have to go out again till Dux came for us. The girls were sitting out in the front yard, and I wheeled the sulky over to a chair. " Isn't it a grand day for the races? " I said, and sat down.

The girls looked at one another and didn't say anything. Buddy reached for me and I undid the sulky strap to let him toddle around. Just then the woman came outside. She picked Buddy up and plunked him back into the sulky, paying no attention to his protests. "Don't you think the air is too cool for him?" she asked me.

"Goodness, no! He's use to being outdoors."

"Maybe so, but —" She smiled and put a hand on my shoulder. "Look, dearie, you'd best go upstairs. We — well, we're expectin' company and there ain't enough chairs," she finished lamely.

I don't have to be knocked down to take a hint! I grabbed Buddy up in my arms, pushed the sulky out of the way, went inside, and slammed the screen door behind me, trying to swallow the lump in my throat. Buddy kissed my wet cheek as I stalked up the stairs. "Never mind. We don't care if they don't like us. Daddy'll be here soon," I gulped. But it hurt just the same.

I fed my baby and put him to bed for his nap. Then I ate half a sandwich, packed our belongings, and spent the next hour looking out the window feeling sorry for myself. Suddenly I jumped up, thinking I had heard Dux's voice. I looked at my watch and saw that it was only three o'clock, but then I was sure it was his engineering boots stomping up the stairs — no one in all the world walks quite like Dux! I flung open the door, my arms wide. Dux pushed me aside, scooped Buddy up from the bed, grabbed my suitcase, and glared at me.

"Get your hat and get the heck out of here!" he exploded.

"But, Dux — you haven't even kissed me!"

"Do as I tell you," he barked, and started out the door.

I got my hat and coat, picked up the few toys, and followed him down the stairway, fighting against tears.

In the lower hall he motioned for me to get the sulky and opened the front door. Even though I'd paid for the room, I wanted to thank the woman for taking me in, though she had acted as if she regretted it, but he pushed me out and stalked to the car. The gears clashed as the Ford shot forward.

" What in the world is the matter with you, Dux? " I flared. " What are you so mad about? "

The muscles in his square jaw tightened and his face paled with anger. " Ye gods! I can't let you out of my sight! " He stopped at a corner to let traffic pass and glared at me. " You don't even know where you were! "

" W-what do you mean? " I stammered.

The car jerked forward. " You were in a whore house! " he yelled. " That's what I mean."

The horror of his words stung me speechless as we drove down the tree-shaded street. Then a question bobbed into my mind, but when I looked at the white knuckles of Dux's hands on the steering wheel, I decided for once to keep still.

We never spoke of it again, but I've often wondered, *How did he know?*

IO

WE SPENT SATURDAY and Sunday at a little hotel off the beaten path and Dux left for the office Monday morning. In the afternoon I took Buddy to Dr. Fulton, feeling that it was an unnecessary expense, for since a tooth popped through over the week end he'd been so full of vim and vigor it was hard to hold him in check.

"Nothing wrong with this young man," Dr. Fulton said, pushing a skull-and-bones paperweight farther out of reach of my son's predatory hands. "Unless it's too much curiosity," he added, smiling at me.

We left for Tompkinsville on Tuesday and pulled into the Deans' field about five o'clock in the afternoon. As we stopped in front of our tents, Mrs. Dean came hurrying down, wanting to know about the baby and what the doctor said. "Did you tell him about the worms?" she asked.

"He checked Buddy from head to toe," I evaded, not wanting to hurt her feelings. "Said he's in perfect health."

She looked at me for a minute as if she didn't quite believe the doctor's verdict, then smiled. "Well, that's good. You all come up to supper," she said. "I 'lowed you'd be in tonight, so I made grits and fried apples, knowing how you love 'em."

Buddy reached his arms to her, "Hi, Dean. Hi, Dean."

She picked him up and hugged him. " You're a good boy." He nodded vigorously. " Dood boy," he repeated, his arms around her neck.

When we went inside the house, Benny was unloading an armful of firewood into the box behind the kitchen stove. He straightened, flashed a welcome smile, and came toward us with outstretched hands.

" Shore glad you folks are back," he said, completely sober for once.

" Glad to be back, Benny," Dux said. " And I'm especially glad to find you . . . this way! "

Benny grinned a little sheepishly. " Well, I bin thinkin' on your words and I reckon you're plumb right. It's my bounden duty to he'p my woman — I know she's bin right worried." He looked across at his wife standing in front of the stove. " Don't seem to hanker for the jug no more — leastways, not much — " He stopped and his face turned a brick-red. I couldn't help feeling sorry for him. He seemed so lovable when he was humble like this, and I could see why Mrs. Dean had stood by him all these years.

Dux slapped him on the back. " Atta boy, Ben! "

Mrs. Dean crammed two sticks of wood into the firebox of the big range, clanked the door shut, and wiped her eyes on the corner of her apron. " Benny's broke up a new patch o' ground down by the creek," she said tremulously, her face flushed from the heat, her eyes bright with hope. " He's aimin' for to have a truck garden."

" Yep," Benny said with a jerk of his head. " I figger a fellow kin do right well with, say, sweet corn, termaters, yams, an' beans. Might even put in sorghum cane, make my own molasses," he added, thoughtfully.

" You're absolutely right," Dux said. " You could probably grow anything in this rich dirt; you're lucky to have such good farm land."

105

Mrs. Dean, refusing my offer to help, bustled around putting the " vittles " on the table, then took the big coffeepot from the stove and filled four cups. She poured a glass of milk for Buddy, lifted him into the improvised high chair, and motioned to us. " Come set. There's plenty of it — such as 'tis," she added modestly.

We sat down to succulent fried ham, red gravy, candied yams, corn pone, and homemade jams — not to mention the extra fried apples and hominy grits. As we ate, we listened to Benny tell how " taters " should be planted in the light of the moon and what seed corn produced the best roasting ears.

" This ham is delicious, Mrs. Dean," I said, reaching for a second helping.

She nodded. " I told you there was nothin' wrong with that meat. 'Twould have been a sin to throw it away."

I stared at her in dismay. " Y-you mean this is the ham Dad sent? The one with the — er — s-skippers? " I stammered, dropping the platter back on the table.

" That's right," she beamed. " Best ham I ever et — skippers or no."

My stomach turned over and my hand flew to my mouth. Mrs. Dean's quick assurance that the meat had been carefully washed and thoroughly cooked was no help. I ran for the door, reaching the back yard just in the nick of time.

Later, when we were home and getting ready for bed, Dux burst out laughing. He'd been grinning all evening, but I had tried not to notice it. " If only you could have seen your face! " he chortled.

" Oh, shut up, you — you cannibal! " I threw my shoe at him, still sick at the thought of sharing ham with a *worm!* Dux had eaten the ghastly stuff too, and it didn't seem to bother him. " You must have a stomach of cast iron," I snapped.

Afterward, Mrs. Dean and I laughed about it, but it certainly wasn't funny at the time. It was months before I could eat home-cured ham with any degree of relish — and even today I cringe at the very sight of a wriggly white worm.

That summer Buddy grew strong and sturdy, and the flowers I'd planted flourished, despite Mrs. Dean's repeated warnings that I was killing the young plants with kindness. Buddy and I spent hours hauling fertilizer in his little red wagon, digging and watering, and making bouquets for the table. Mrs. Dean also thought it silly of me to use white tablecloths every day, but somehow oilcloth didn't seem worthy of my lovely centerpiece of zinnias, sweet peas, and bachelor-buttons. And anyway old Mrs. Hawkins, at whose house Dux dropped my laundry every Monday on his way to the job, needed the work.

" I just can't get enough washin'," was her way of putting it. " Jest that crazy about my new gasoline washer. Never figgered I'd have it so easy."

I was proud of my tent home that Dux had built, proud of my son, my flowers, and my newly acquired accomplishments as a homemaker. I had learned how to cook — really cook. The trial-and-error days were behind me. And I'd learned how to sew. Dux's pants " snugged " his hips and he seemed proud of telling people that I'd made them.

It's a good life, I told myself time and time again, counting my blessings. Never mind the isolation, the primitive aspects; we're building a future, a future of security and happiness. And yet there were times when I wished for someone to whom I could say, " It's a good life," and prove it. Dux knew without being told. And the Deans, for all their friendliness, saw life mainly in its harsh realities.

Mother and Dad had promised to come for a visit bringing Drexel and the baby, but Mother still couldn't walk without help and her doctor advised against the trip. Mother and Father Gentry had planned to come, but one of the grandchildren became ill and Mother Gentry felt she was needed.

Then, one Sunday in September, the Addisons surprised us with a visit. They suggested they take us into Tompkinsville for dinner, but I remembered the flies in the sorghum at the Newberry Hotel, and anyway I wanted to show off my culinary skill, though I'd have preferred more time for preparations.

" If you don't mind eating late," I told them, " I'll get you a dinner a lot better than that hotel."

They looked a little skeptical, but Dux grinned and said: " She can do it too. No fooling."

Dux took Mr. Addison out on the porch to talk business. Mrs. Addison played with Buddy, and I scurried around getting things together for as festive a meal as time would permit.

At four o'clock we sat down to golden fried chicken — Mrs. Dean had taken two from her brood, killed and dressed them for me — lettuce and tomatoes from Benny's garden, potatoes and squash. There were also piping hot biscuits, my own strawberry preserves, and a huckleberry pie. Not bad, I thought, for a hurry-up meal; Miss Abby would have been proud of me.

Dux must have read my thoughts word for word for he beamed and said, " Not bad for a quick meal, Shortie."

" Not bad? " Mr. Addison repeated. " That's an understatement if there ever was one." Smiling, he turned to me. " Best dinner I've had in a long time! "

Mrs. Addison added her endorsement, and Dux reached across and patted my hand. The proof of the dinner, however, was in the eating, and if I'd had any doubts on that score they were instantly dispelled when they all took second helpings. Later, when we scraped and stacked the almost empty platter and bowls, I thought of that other time when I'd cooked, or tried to cook, for Dux's boss and wished that Mr. Yates could eat one of my dinners now. I smiled when I recalled what a miserable flop that first company meal had been. What had seemed like tragedy when it happened was just another amusing incident now when seen in retrospect.

Mrs. Addison, pretty in blue silk with one of my frilliest aprons tied around her slim waist, brushed the crumbs from the table and set my bowl of early chrysanthemums back in the center.

"They're lovely," she said. "You must have a green thumb."

"No," I laughed. "It's Benny's manure — and I'm just lucky, I guess. I love this place. It's home."

They left shortly afterward, and we stood on our porch waving good-by. Then Dux turned to me and said abruptly: "We're moving, honey — to Maytown. Addison just told me. We finished the last contract well yesterday, and they need all the rigs and contractors they can get in the Maytown field."

My heart sank. Maybe I wasn't so lucky, after all. "Oh, Dux, how soon must we go?"

"I heard of a rig in Cumberland Valley that I think we can buy cheap. I'll go look at it and probably be gone a couple of days; that'll give you time to pack up." He tried to be nonchalant about it, then put his arms around me. "I know how you feel, baby. I hate to leave here too."

He couldn't know, I thought. No man could. Looking across the field at the grape arbor in the Deans' yard, I thought of the jelly we'd intended to make this week, the rompers half finished on Mrs. Dean's sewing machine, the fall flowers blooming furiously around the tents. The other moves hadn't been the same. Leaving here was different. Just as I'd told Mrs. Addison, this was home.

The Dux Oil Company, Dux said, was being dissolved, the original investment paid back, and the balance divided among the stockholders. Our part wasn't much, but it was more money than we'd ever had at one time before, and Dux felt that the experience he'd gained couldn't have been counted in dollars and cents.

"Can't we wait about going to Maytown — just a little while?" I bit my lip, wishing I hadn't said that. Dux wasn't one to wait when there was a job to be done.

He shook his head. "No. Louisville Gas has started a producing company in eastern Kentucky. They've got some important leases in Floyd County, around Maytown, and unless drilling is commenced on schedule, they'll lose them."

In this case his first assignment had all the earmarks of a message-to-Garcia affair with a time limit. Mr. Addison told him if he could find a large steam-driven rig that could be bought reasonably, it would be put to work immediately, along with the two others, on a contract basis.

"If I buy it, move it on location, and get the drilling started before the lease runs out," Dux told me, grinning wryly, "that'll mean just two weeks for the entire operation."

"Oh, you'll do it. You always have," I said, looking at the doubtful expression on his face. "Want to bet on it?"

"No." He shook his head, though he did look pleased at my expression of confidence in him. "There's always a first time, Shortie — besides, you're prejudiced."

"Of course you won't bet," I grinned. "You'd lose because you'd win."

As it developed he would have lost the bet, because he did get the rig in operation on schedule, even with a little time to spare, though it required some doing on his part. As luck would have it, the outfit was practically as good as new and just the type needed. In a way, that rig was a symbol of lost hope, as it had been used by a promotional group to drill a well that proved to be only a dry hole. The derrick was still up, the tools hanging, the boiler connected — just as the drillers had left them when the project was abandoned.

On the surface it looked like a fine proposition, but there were plenty of hurdles to be overcome. In the first place, there was the matter of dismantling, requiring considerable time — and time was one commodity there was too little of. There were also the matters of distance, of inaccessibility, and of moving, details that were not to be dismissed lightly in view of the time element involved.

The rig was located about seven miles from the Cumberland River, up a creek in a very rugged part of the country. The nearest railroad was some sixty miles away, and the only possible way to get the equipment out of there was to move it down to the Cumberland River, then barge it up to Burnside, Kentucky, where it would be loaded on flatcars and shipped.

" Seems you picked yourself a lulu," I said to Dux when he told me about it later.

" No. Except for the timing, it would have been a comparatively simple matter — just dismantling, moving, setting up — "

" Oh, you and your eternal belittling," I bantered. " To hear you tell it, everything's simple. Only I know very well it's not so."

" But this was," he insisted. " Or rather it would have been — if it hadn't been for the transportation problem. That really was a lulu, as you call it, all along the line."

And it must have been, what with the assembling of

enough men — mainly local mountaineers, whom Dux was obliged to round up on horseback — oxen, teams, and wagons. Not to mention the various idiosyncrasies of the Cumberland River that had to be coped with, and the peculiar affinity of freight cars for sidings off the beaten path.

In that particular section, it seemed, the river was navigable only during spasmodic flood periods. And so it was necessary to do the dismantling, hauling, and loading simultaneously, in order to beat the anticipated shallowness. It was a matter of quick action while the river was up and the steamboat still running.

" Sort of like rubbing your head and patting your stomach at one and the same time," Dux acknowledged, laughing. " The river was falling — and fast. I hired as many men and teams as I could find and we started tearing the rig down, sending it piecemeal to the river. I'd agreed to have the whole thing there by sundown the day the steamship company set as a deadline — "

" And you did, of course," I prompted, knowing I'd have to pull the story out of Dux if I was ever to know it. He was never one to go in for personal hornblowing, even to me.

He shrugged, as if to dismiss the entire matter as inconsequential. " Sure we did. I said we would. Truth is, we had it all there by noon, but it took the steamboat crew and our crew till midnight to load it aboard. There were over seventy tons. By that time, the river was falling — and fast.

" The steamer made Burnside, but only after it had scraped bottom several times," Dux went on to explain. " Then it was loaded on flatcars, taken to Floyd County, and hauled four miles to the leases." Even the flatcars had to be watched, lest they be switched off to some siding en route and delay the process so that the leases would have to be forfeited.

But the operation was a success, and the rig was up on the lease, doing its stuff in a rather spectacular way, a full day and a half before the contracts expired!

II

EARLY IN OCTOBER we said good-by to the Deans, and it was a moment full of emotion for us all. Mrs. Dean and I frankly cried when I tried to find words to thank her for her kindness and the wonderful things she had taught me. " We'll come back someday," I promised, " if we possibly can."

Benny looked thin and drawn, but he was sober. His eyes were misty when he clasped Dux's hand. " You done more for me than my own kin," he said. " A no-good cuss like me . . . I wisht I could thank ye — " His voice broke and for a moment I was afraid he was going to cry too.

Dux put an arm across his shoulders. " You're a good guy, Benny," he said gently. " You've only got one fault — and you'll whip that. I know you can do it, Ben."

I wasn't so sure about that. Benny's falls from grace were as much a part of him as his lank, scrawny figure; his periods of remorse as natural to him as his wife's unfailing forgiveness. Poor Mrs. Dean, I thought; she'll be forgiving and hoping for the rest of her life. I wondered who would bail Benny out the next time he got into trouble. And there would always be a next time, because trouble followed Benny just as surely as a geologist followed anticlines.

As the car backed out of the driveway, I stared at the spot where our tents had been. My colorful flowers, bordering an empty square out in the field, looked lonely, and it seemed to me that the heads of my marigolds drooped just a bit. I tore my eyes away from the scene to glance down at the old chamber pot between my feet on the floor of the car. The begonia I'd potted months ago was all I had left of my first real home.

We reached Louisville late in the afternoon and drove to the Addisons', where we were to spend the night. Our few household belongings were being shipped for storage in a room over their garage. I loved visiting the Addisons. Aside from their warm hospitality, their house fulfilled all my storybook notions of glamour and my sense of sectional pride. It had been the home of the " Little Colonel," and still retained much of the original atmosphere. Set back at the end of a cul-de-sac bordered by giant trees, it was typical of the Old South both in architecture and feeling.

As a girl, I had laughed and cried over the " Little Colonel " series, written by Annie Fellows Johnston, a Louisville woman. And so it was like a trip down Memory Lane — just wandering through the big rooms, admiring the quaint antiques, re-creating the stories and picturing the scenes that the silent walls must have witnessed.

When dinner was over and Buddy put to bed, the four of us sat down to an evening of bridge — or so Mrs. Addison and I hoped. But after listening an hour to talk about river crossings, pipelines, and rigs, in between such questions as " What's trumps? " and " Oh, is it my turn to deal? " we gave up, and left the men to continue their conversation, but I doubt if they even missed us.

The next morning Mr. Addison took us to the train. Dux had turned the Company car in, since the roads in

Floyd County were said to be allergic to automobiles. A man met us at the Maytown station, took us out to the camp that had been set up for contractors and workmen. It consisted of a big tent used for meals and a group of smaller ones for sleeping quarters. A tent was assigned to us, but after a restless night on an Army cot, I started looking for a place to stay.

It was no small feat finding a place, what with wheeling the sulky along dirt roads and Buddy just at the age when he wanted to get out and push. Too, available rooms in the Maytown area were conspicuous mainly for their absence.

Finally, after three days of looking, I persuaded a woman to rent us a bedroom, promising to do the cleaning myself and to keep Buddy from the rest of the house. She lived a short piece from the camp, so we continued to take our meals there — an unhappy situation for me, because I was in the beginning of my second pregnancy and bothered with morning sickness.

Although I took pride in my husband's accomplishments, life in Maytown, from my point of view, soon became a rather dreary existence. With little to do, I spent hours feeling sorry for myself, wondering why oil and gas wells had to be at the end of civilization, worrying about bringing up babies in the middle of nowhere, no matter what it might mean to Dux's career. So absorbed was I in my own fancied misery that this might have gone on indefinitely — but then something happened to make me realize that I didn't know when I was well off.

Dux had brought in one gasser and was in the process of moving the rig to another location when one of the superintendents of the field asked him to supervise the tubing of another well. This was a rather extraordinary request, as contractors did not usually leave a well at tubing time.

" But this is an emergency; I have to go to Prestonsburg

on urgent business," the man explained, and so Dux agreed to take over during his absence.

He had eaten an early breakfast and left, taking his lunch with him. After cleaning our room, I spent most of the morning stitching playful ducks and solemn-looking bunny rabbits on rompers for Buddy, while he entertained himself with his toys. At lunch time we got his little red wagon, gathered up a few toys and my sewing kit, and went over to the camp. I would have to wait there for the washwoman to bring my clothes, and the wagon would be needed to haul the fresh laundry back to our room. Buddy loved the idea of being helpful, and his chubby hands would grip the wagon tongue importantly.

We had scarcely finished our lunch when the washwoman came. I strapped the clothesbasket to the wagon, placed my sewing kit on top, picked the toys up in my arms, and told Buddy to come on. But at that moment a commotion outside told me that something out of the ordinary was happening. Dropping the toys, I ran to the entrance of the tent just in time to see two men carefully lifting a third man off the back of a mule.

" What's happened? " I cried. My voice broke as I recognized my husband, a strange, pitiable Dux I'd never seen before. His face was black and contorted with pain, his arms hung limp, and he leaned heavily on the two men as they led him into the tent.

" It — it's all right, Shortie. I — I'm just burned a little," Dux said through swollen lips, then collapsed on a cot.

With an effort I pulled myself together, breathed a silent prayer, and knelt beside Dux.

" Get hot water and soda from the kitchen," I said to the cook, standing nearby, wringing his hands helplessly. " And keep people out of here. Get my scissors from my sewing bag — it's in the little wagon on top of the clothesbasket," I told one of the men who had helped Dux into the tent. " Go get Dr. Allen — hurry! " I said to the other.

With hands that were miraculously sure and steady, I began to cut the pull-over sweater away from Dux's pitifully burned flesh, forcing back the tears that were burning my eyelids. He stirred, opened his eyes, and mumbled something. I leaned closer.

" What is it, darling? "

" Don't cut — " Breathing heavily, he tried to raise his head, but the effort was too much for him and he sank back against the pillows.

" Lie still, Dux," I said gently. " Don't try to talk. Dr. Allen will be here soon."

" Don't cut — " he said again. He raised one arm, looked at it, then at me, and I understood. He had been so proud of the sweater I'd knitted for him last year. I had done it under protest, because I knew so little about knitting — actually, he had nagged me into doing it.

" Oh, my darling," I choked. " I'll knit you another sweater — dozens of them! "

By the time I had finished cutting the sweater away, the cook came with a bucket of warm water and a bowl of baking soda. I ran to the clothesbasket to get some clean diapers — Buddy still wore them at night — and only then did I remember my son. He'd scattered most of my clean clothes all over the dirt floor of the tent, but there was no time to think of that. I grabbed a handful of things from the basket and hurried back to Dux. Bathing his face, hands, and arms carefully, I patted them dry with a soft cloth, then sprinkled soda as thickly as possible onto the raw flesh.

" You should have gone to a hospital, Gentry," Dr. Allen grumbled when he came inside the tent a little while later. " The others did. They wondered what had become of you."

Dr. Allen took over. The cook offered to take care of Buddy, so I stayed close to Dux in case there was something I could do. But when Dr. Allen began cutting the proud flesh away, I gasped and ran my hand over my eyes. He glanced up at me.

" Get my bag over there," he snapped. " Take out three rolls of wide bandage and a roll of adhesive tape."

Trying to shake off the dizziness, I managed to do as he told me.

" Now," he barked at me without looking up. " Get those scissors and start cutting strips of adhesive about a foot long. Stick the ends on the back of this chair."

" Will — will he be all right? " I was almost afraid to ask. Dux looked much too still — though I'd seen Dr. Allen give him a hypodermic.

" He'll be fine, barring the unexpected," he said gently. " Anyone tell you what happened? "

" No," I said. " The men helped him off a mule when he got here, but they didn't know."

" The well caught fire. Some damn fool must have struck a match. Any idea why this man of yours rode mule-back three quarters of a mile instead of going to a hospital with the others? "

" No," I said again. " I didn't even know there were others."

" Five. Met old Hank Lucas about twenty minutes after it happened — he told me. Said Dux kept saying he had to get to you before someone scared you. Afraid you'd mark the baby." The doctor laughed shortly. " Someone's been telling him old wives' tales."

Tears spilled out of my eyes and I wiped them away with the back of my hand. It was like Dux, I thought, to consider others before himself. Oh, why did he have to do this dangerous work? Why couldn't we live like other people? All I ever wanted was a home, a place to be happy in, a place to bring our children up.

" Give him one of these pills every hour," Dr. Allen was saying. " Keep him quiet until the men come from work tonight, then have them move him to your room."

I nodded and took the medicine. He picked up his bag and gave me a pat on the shoulder. " You keep your chin up," he said, smiling. " I'll drop around in the morning."

Dux was restless and in pain during the long, still night and neither of us slept much. I turned the lamp down low and lay staring at the ceiling. All I could think of was: What if he'd been burned to death? It could so easily have happened.

I wasn't cut out for a pioneer woman, I decided. Women used to pick up and leave everything they loved to go west with their men, to build a new country — to make progress, as Miss Abby used to say. They weren't afraid.

But I am, I confessed miserably. I don't care about progress. I'd rather live in a tent, a log cabin, without cooking or heating with gas, and ride a horse instead of a car, if it means keeping Dux safe.

Dr. Allen came at nine, and, after he left, Dux seemed to feel better, drifting off into a natural sleep. At noon I fed him some broth sent over by the camp cook. His lips were parched and cracked and his head looked like a mummy's. It was swathed completely in bandages, except for the eye slits and his mouth, and his hands were huge mittens of white.

The morning after the second night he even joked with Dr. Allen, and I began to breathe easier. But the next day when the bandages were being changed, I saw the angry red streaks running up his arm, and the anxious frown on

Dr. Allen's face did not escape me. I knew what it meant. Blood poisoning had set in.

We took the afternoon train to Ashland, where an ambulance met us. Dr. Allen went with us to the hospital, and later I took a train for Morehead, where Dad met me to take Buddy home with him. Thinking Buddy might cry, I bought him candy, a banana, chewing gum — everything he shouldn't have had. It was the first time he'd ever left me and I was afraid Dad was in for a rugged time. But when my baby callously walked out the gate, clinging to Dad's hand, not even bothering to wave to me, I burst into tears. Not even a mother, it seemed, was indispensable!

Like most men who have never encountered illness, Dux was by no means a prize patient. In fact, the hospital nurses insisted he was the worst they had ever seen. He hated the place and nothing was right. I spent every waking hour with him, sometimes not going back to my hotel until midnight. I fed him, filled his pipe, and read to him hour upon hour. If I happened to be five minutes late getting to the hospital in the morning, he'd start to quarrel. But he was going to be all right. His disposition proved that. Even the nurses had a word for it: cantankerous. I guess there's no one more difficult than a strong man plagued by sickness and on the road to recovery.

The bath hour, in particular, was anathema to Dux. Not that he was allergic to bathing. For all his familiarity with occupational grime, he had what almost amounted to a fetish for cleanliness. But he didn't like the idea of the nurses " fussing around " at bath time, and made an issue of it right from the start.

I was sitting at his bedside one morning reading to him when a pretty nurse, bright-eyed and efficient in her crisp white uniform, tapped me on the shoulder.

" I must ask you to go outside for a while, Mrs. Gentry,"

she said in a tone of authority. Then she added with what I thought was unnecessary coyness, but which was undoubtedly her idea of the perfect bedside manner,

" The Mister and I are going to have a nice little bath — aren't we, Mr. Gentry? "

" Who — *me?* " Dux sat up straight, though the pain of doing so caused him to wince. Although his lips were so swollen he could hardly talk, in a few telling phrases he managed to convey to the startled young woman that he was having no part of her " nice little bath." In fact, his words were so explosive, his manner so defiant, that I felt a little sorry for the girl as she left the room with more haste than dignity.

Thereafter, there was no interference at bath time. With the permission of the attending physician, it was I who did the honors, took the gaff, until my rebellious patient was able to manage for himself.

Dux was finally allowed to leave the hospital, but was told he must rest another week before going back to work. We went to West Liberty to spend the week with Mother and Dad. Buddy had grown a lot and talked a blue streak, but he didn't seem particularly glad to see us. He would dismiss our attempts to love him with a quick kiss, and wiggle out of our arms. He and young Russell were quite a pair, into everything. What one wouldn't think of, the other would. Frances, mother's hired girl, seemed to love them, but she was usually a wreck at the end of the day.

The house was always full of people coming to see the babies — and they were cute. Dressed alike, both with blond curly hair and blue eyes, they looked more like twins than uncle and nephew. It was fun to watch their antics. Sometimes they'd share their toys, laughing and loving each other. Then — wham! One would push the other down, yelling with rage, and the war would be on. Dux said they'd grow up to be prize fighters, with such an early start. Usually we left them alone to fight out their own battles, for they were pretty well matched.

Mother had at last found a doctor who knew what to do for her. The crutches were discarded and she had shoes made with a brace for her left foot. This doctor insisted that she do something to keep her mind active, so she had gone back to the piano she'd studied as a girl, sometimes practicing three or four hours a day. And she looked a lot better, more like her old self.

It wasn't until we were in the living room the second night after we got in that I learned just what had happened at the gas well. I hadn't really cared as long as Dux was all right. Dad asked if the well was boarded in, as wells usually were in fall and winter.

" Yes, but the door was open," Dux said. " That's what saved us. The force of the explosion blew us right out the door and carried us about thirty feet, over a pile of casing. There were five of us, and we landed in a pile on the ground. My first thought was to cut the belt and save the engine, but by that time it was an inferno. None of us realized we were burned until a few minutes later when the pain started."

" What caused the explosion? " Mother wanted to know.

" The usual thing — carelessness," Dux said. " Some roustabout they'd hired lighted a cigarette. I saw him put it in his mouth and yelled at him. But he couldn't hear me above the noise. I'd been measuring the perforated joint — " he looked at Dad, " you know, the packer that shuts off the salt water and confines the gas in the two-inch tubing. I threw the tape at him just as he struck the match, but it was too late."

" He rode a mule clear into camp — as badly as he was burned," I broke in. " He was afraid someone would get to me first and scare me. Mother, Dr. Allen says you can't mark a baby. It's just an old wives' tale."

" You certainly can mark a baby! " Mother began spiritedly. " Look at Mattie Tillman's boy, Jesse — "

" Wait a minute," Dad interrupted. " Let's hear the rest of this. How big was the well, Dux? "

" Not big," Dux said. " It was flowing salt water mixed with some gas, and the explosion didn't make much noise — a dull thud. Not many people even heard it."

" Then how did you get help? " Mother asked.

" We didn't till we went after it, under our own power. There was a country store at the crossroads below the well and we went there. Mrs. Henry, who runs it, helped us wash our faces and hands in kerosene and put Vicks salve on our burns."

" That must have hurt like the devil," Drexel broke in.

" I'll say it did." Dux made a wry face and continued: " The other fellows were sent to the hospital, but I kept worrying about Winalee. There was a mule hitched to the post in front of the store." He stopped to light his pipe and grinned at us. " I never did find out who owned that mule — or if he ever got him back! "

12

AFTER THANKSGIVING we left West Liberty to go back to Maytown, promising Mother we'd return for Christmas. Dux still seemed a little pale to me, but he could hardly wait to get back on the job, getting more and more restless by the minute, for he was never entirely happy when there was something to be done and he was not doing it.

As soon as we got to Maytown, I went to see about a furnished house I'd heard we could rent. With one baby constantly underfoot, having no place to play, and another on the way, I felt the need for more space. A furnished room was much too cramped for comfortable living, and eating our meals at the camp was not my idea of home-making.

I'd been told about the house on the day of the explosion, but of course Dux's injuries made me forget everything else. It was not too far from the wells, had three bedrooms, a big yard for Buddy to play in, and a real fireplace. Upon investigation, I found it was still available, but the rent was more than we could afford.

However, I refused to be defeated. I wanted that house and was determined to have it, even if it meant taking roomers. And I was lucky. Mr. Van Patten, a field super-intendent who lived at the camp and was as fed up on it as we were, agreed to take one of the rooms; his secretary,

Nancy Powers from Prestonsburg, took another, leaving the large bedroom to Dux, Buddy, and me. I hired a cook and we moved in, the expenses being divided three ways. I was the only deadhead — but then I was the one who looked after everything and paid Rose, the hired girl.

It was a pleasant arrangement, although, like all my previous " homes," it was to last only a little while. We called it our clubhouse, and it was fun planning meals, keeping house. Dux even found an old sewing machine in the attic and fixed it up so that Nancy and I could do a bit of sewing.

Often on the long winter evenings, after Buddy was put to bed, the four of us would gather in front of the fireplace. Sometimes we'd roast chestnuts, pop corn, make fudge, or play cards on the marble-top center table. When the weather grew warmer, we'd sit on the front porch, Nancy and I listening absently while the two men " talked shop," sometimes falling asleep while their voices went on, on, and on.

Then, suddenly, it was all over. By the last of April our work in the Maytown area was finished. The gas wells were completed and connected to pipelines, and Dux was asked to come into Louisville for another assignment. Once more we left our home, saying good-by to friends we might never see again. With the exception of our clothes, all we had to take with us were snapshots, Buddy's crib, my old pot of begonia that I insisted on carrying, and our memories.

We reached Louisville at noon on Friday and took a taxi to the Seelbach. Dux went to the Gas Company office and I went to bed with Buddy. It was getting close to the time of my confinement, and the train ride had tired me. Goodness only knows, I thought, where'll we go next. But at least I'd be in Louisville until after the baby came. I glanced at the newspaper on the table, then pushed it aside. For once, Dux would have to find us a place to live — I just wasn't up to chasing want ads.

With the help of Mrs. Addison, Dux found a small apartment that wasn't bad. Mrs. Bell, the woman who was to take care of Buddy and Dux while I was in the hospital, moved in with us. She had been there a week, sleeping on the couch in the living room, building up expense, and still no baby. Mrs. Bell was sure it would be a boy because I came to a point in front, and Mrs. Addison was just as certain it would be a girl because I carried it low. At first I'd dreamed of a little girl — since learning to sew — but now I didn't care, just so it was a baby and had all its fingers and toes!

Finally one Saturday, in the middle of the night, I went to the hospital. A few hours later, still drugged, I heard Dux's far-off voice calling, " Winalee . . . darling, wake up." I managed to get one eye open, heard him laugh with a funny little catch in his throat, felt his lips on my cheek.

" You have a daughter, honey — a *beautiful* little girl! "

I tried to smile, tried to look at him, but it was too much of an effort, and I drifted off into a deliciously painless sleep.

Dux named her Winalee after me, but Buddy called her " Baby Sis." She really was a beautiful baby, with big blue eyes and curly auburn hair. I could hardly wait to get home and start sewing for her. For hours I would lie with her small body cradled in my arm, just looking at her, thinking ahead, and wishing I could pour all the good things of the world into those tiny pink palms.

When Baby Sis was a month old, I let Mrs. Bell go. She was wonderful with Buddy and I missed her terribly, but we just couldn't afford the fifteen dollars a week it was costing us. Dux helped me a lot. He dressed Buddy in the mornings, gave the baby her six o'clock bottle, and changed her pants — even though it made him sick every time he did it. For a man who could eat a piece of ham that a worm had chewed on, that struck me as funny. " Gagging at a gnat and swallowing a camel," I told him.

One Friday Dux came home at noon, a thing he seldom did. I had just put the children down for naps and was carrying the waxing mop to the living room when I heard his whistle and threw open the door.

" Hi! What are you doing home this time of day? " I greeted him.

He hugged me, then looked away. " Maybe I came home just to kiss you," he answered evasively.

" Unh-unh." I shook my head, stood the mop against the wall, and started for the kitchen. " Come on. I'll fix you a sandwich while you tell me about it. There's coffee left from my lunch."

He followed me, sat down at the table, and lighted a cigarette. " Addison wants me to go to Ivyton — wants me to finish up that gas field there."

I cut a thin slice of light bread, spread it with butter, and forked a piece of country ham from the platter in the icebox. " I thought it was too good to be true — getting to live in Louisville, I mean."

" But, honey — " Dux began.

" Oh, I don't really mind," I said, placing the sandwich in front of him and pouring his coffee. " When do we leave? "

" That's just it, darling." He hesitated a moment, then pushed the sandwich away from him. " I — well, I can't take you."

It was like a slap in the face. " Can't take me? " I gasped. " What do you mean, you can't take me? "

" Look, dear." He pulled me down on his lap and tried

to explain. " This place is wild. They've sent men up there twice, and every time they tried to lay pipelines there was trouble. What I mean is — well, the natives say it with guns. It's no place for you and the babies, Shortie."

" That's downright silly! " I flared. " Ivyton is only about thirty miles from West Liberty. Civilized people just don't act that way."

" You don't know how rugged that Kentucky hill country is," he said. " Anyway, I'd rather look things over first."

" Dux, that's the craziest thing I ever heard," I exclaimed. " After all, *I'm* a Kentuckian. I'm a hillbilly myself — and I *know*. Why, there was a girl at Hamilton from Salyersville — and that's only a little piece from Ivyton — "

" It's seven miles. But don't get me wrong, honey. I think Kentuckians are the salt of the earth, but the fact remains that in some parts they're apt to make their own laws — and they don't like outsiders."

" That may be true way back in the hills," I conceded. " But not that close to my town. Why, we've sent Senators and Congressmen from our district, and Miss Leonabelle Harris even had a book published about the beauty and character and dignity of Kentucky! " I stopped, but only to catch my breath for a fresh start.

" And if you think I can't take it — primitive living, I mean — then you really are crazy," I accused. " You've got to admit I did fairly well at Tompkinsville."

" All right, all right, honey. You don't have to sell *me*. Kentucky's a fine place and you're a grand little sport. I know all that. But just the same I want you to stay right here till I come back for you."

I put my head on his shoulder and began to cry. The thought of separation from Dux was too much for me. I knew, from what he had said, that the job at Ivyton was a challenge to him. And if there was any danger — although I was unwilling to admit that — surely my place was with him.

That did it. Like so many strong men, Dux was peculiarly vulnerable to tears — my tears. And so a week later we were on our way to Ivyton. We left what we couldn't take with us in the Addisons' garage, where the rest of our belongings were stored. I gave my precious begonia plant to Mrs. Addison, though I don't think she cared for the pot. We had our hands full, what with Buddy, Baby Sis, a pillow, diaper bag, bottles, and lunch box.

We checked our suitcases as far as Paintsville, where we were to change to a little old lumber train that would take us the last eighteen miles to Ivyton, in Magoffin County. The coach wasn't crowded, so we had plenty of room. Turning the plush seats to face each other, I put Baby Sis on the pillow and she slept most of the way. Dux sat opposite with Buddy, counting cows and horses and watching telephone poles rush by.

It was picturesque country, made up of deep forests, hillside farms, and lazy rivers winding through blue-green valleys. True, some of the houses were log cabins or shacks on run-down land where people eked out a precarious existence. But here and there were evidences of prosperity in lovely white farmhouses with huge white barns, fertile fields, and green pastures where Holsteins, Jerseys, and other fine cattle grazed contentedly.

I smiled to myself and thought, How could anyone possibly be afraid in such peaceful surroundings? Of course there would always be tales of Kentucky gun fights and bloodshed, I conceded mentally, remembering a woman I'd met in Brooklyn when we'd stayed with Dux's people during our honeymoon.

" Oh — so you're from Kentucky? " she'd said, looking down her nose at me. " I've always wanted to visit that wild and woolly state, but I'd be afraid to carry a gun. Have you ever seen any of the — er — hillbillies, my dear? "

" Yes," I answered with sudden defiance. " *I'm* a hillbilly. All my people are hillbillies. But we only shoot one another. We don't mess with foreigners, so you wouldn't need to worry." I had to say it, though I hated myself for doing so. I just couldn't help it.

We rode in the caboose from Paintsville to Ivyton, for there were no coaches on the lumber train. And, in spite of the soot and dirt, it was quite an adventure — especially for Dux and Buddy.

In Ivyton, the Gas Company had put up an Aladdin portable house the year before, and this was to be our new home. It had a telephone and was furnished — after a fashion. I began picturing all the things that could be done for it — the bright curtains I'd make, my own pictures on the wall, and bouquets of flowers. It wasn't too late to plant seeds for fall blooming.

We unpacked what we needed, put Baby Sis to bed on the couch, with chairs alongside it to keep her from rolling off, and pushed a bed for Buddy against the wall. Their own beds would come with the barrels of dishes and things we'd shipped. When they were bedded down, we went to the kitchen, made coffee, and ate the sandwiches that were left from our lunch. Dux had little to say and I could tell that he was nervous.

" I wish you'd taken the children and gone to your mother's," he said presently.

" Golly, let's not start that again," I said, and changed the subject. " You'll have to watch the babies in the morning while I go to the store for groceries. I'll start making a list now." I found a piece of wrapping paper, borrowed Dux's pencil, and wrote, " Sugar, flour, salt . . ."

" I'll go now," he offered. " It's only seven o'clock. Country stores usually stay open for a while."

I nodded. He sat silently until I finished, then got up and tucked my list into his shirt pocket. " Don't worry if I'm late getting back," he told me. " I want to find out all I can."

The next day I dressed the babies in their best, brushed their hair into ringlets, put Baby Sis on a pillow in the sulky, and set out to do a little reconnoitering on my own. It was a typical Kentucky June day, comfortably warm, sunny, with the smell of fresh-cut hay in the air. As I wheeled the sulky down the rutty road toward the village, Buddy toddling along beside me, I smiled again at the idea of anything evil happening in such a peacefully prosaic spot. Never mind the ugly rumors, I thought; friendliness begets friendliness — just wait till they see how folksy we are! Dux is wrong. They'd never, never in the world, try to drive *him* away.

Ivyton, I discovered, consisted of a post office, a blacksmith's, a barbershop, and a general store which sold everything from harness to corsets.

The wide door was open and I pulled the sulky inside, Buddy toddling behind me. I had seen general stores before, but in all my life I had never seen such a variety of things assembled together under one roof. Shoes, with their laces or buttons fastened to strings, hung from the low rafters along with pots and pans. Gum boots, saddle pockets, and straw hats were displayed on wooden brackets nailed on the walls, with milk pails, churns, washtubs, and plowshares on the floor below.

On one side of the room, behind a scarred wooden counter, were shelves filled with yard goods, interspersed with overalls, socks, and red woolen underwear. Matching shelves on the opposite side displayed canned goods, a hoop of cheese, and quantities of plug tobacco, with country hams, bacon, and side meat suspended from the topmost shelf. In front of the counter were the inevitable kegs of nails and barrels of brown sugar and soda crackers.

There was also the usual meeting place for men, in the front of the room. It consisted of a potbellied stove, several cane-bottom chairs, and upended kegs. A long box of saw-dust nearby with blobs of tobacco juice around it gave mute testimony that the spitters of Ivyton weren't any too accurate. Three men sat talking, one whittling on a stick of wood with a pocket knife, and two women were finger-ing a piece of cloth, chatting together. When I came through the door with my brood, all conversation stopped and everyone turned to look at us.

" Hi, folks — isn't it a wonderful day? " I said, de-termined to get off on the right foot with my new neigh-bors.

They just stared at us, as if we were something out of a circus, and didn't move. Undaunted, I wheeled the sulky a little closer and Buddy darted to a jar of gumdrops on the counter, reaching for the lid.

" No, honey," I said. " Look at the nice things, but don't touch." I turned to the bearded storekeeper, who leaned across the counter, seemingly as inarticulate as the others. " You certainly have a nice store — just about everything a body would want," I continued with determined bright-ness, hoping to break through his reserve.

" Cat got his tongue, Mommy," Buddy chirped.

" S-sh, darling." I put a hand over my little son's mouth. " Let Mommy do the talking. He's only a baby," I said to the man. " And you know how children are — "

" What do you want, ma'am? " he said, never taking his eyes from my face.

I looked at the shelves behind him, trying wildly to think

133

of something I could buy that wasn't on the list I'd given Dux.

" Jelly! " I announced triumphantly, " Yes — jelly. We love it on hot biscuits! "

The expression on his face made my cheeks burn. " Don't have no call for such. Women in these parts make their own," he said scornfully.

" Well — thanks anyway," I said, wondering what in the world I was thanking him for. Somehow I got out the door and went back to the house, a taste of defeat in my mouth. They can't *all* be like that, I told myself firmly, and made up my mind that before we left this place they'd change their attitude toward us.

Dux had hired local men to build roads to new well locations and to work on the rigs. He was also getting ready to lay pipelines, although it was clear that he was still apprehensive.

" Don't you believe those stories were exaggerated? " I asked hopefully. " I'm sure these are good people — a little standoffish, it's true, but that's because we're strangers and they aren't used to our ways. Imagine your being afraid for me to come here! "

" Maybe I was wrong," Dux conceded reluctantly. " But I know now what the trouble was — why they don't like any outsider whose business is oil or gas."

" You do? " I said, surprised.

He nodded. " They feel they've been gypped — and I'm inclined to agree with them. Seth Higgins, one of the mountaineers I hired, told me the whole story."

According to Seth, Dux went on to explain, some fifteen years before a group of politicians from the county seat had told the local people they would drill for oil if they could acquire enough leases to make the project worthwhile. So the mountaineers, getting together, had signed papers — or made their marks — under the impression that they were only leasing their land and would reap adequate profit.

"Actually," Dux added, shaking his head in disapproval of such unfair tactics, "they had been duped into signing deeds to their mineral rights."

"Why, that's terrible!" I exclaimed. "No wonder they're resentful."

"Yes," Dux agreed. "They didn't really know what they'd done till that first oil well was brought in over in Elliott County. The companies that came to geologize got abstracts — then found that all the mineral rights belonged to a coal company."

"Wasn't there anything the natives could do?"

"Apparently not. After the contractors drilled in a few gas wells, which were bought by our Company, and our men started to pipe it off, the fat was in the fire. They saw everything going out and nothing coming in. So they got mad — started shooting the pipe full of holes. Ran our men away and — "

"I don't blame them one bit. For getting mad, I mean," I qualified hastily.

"No, you can't really blame them. But that doesn't help us. I wish I could make them realize it's not the Gas Company's fault or mine. We're about ready to start laying the pipeline, and it's up to me to figure out some way of winning their confidence. It's my job," he added gravely.

Not only was it Dux's job, I thought, watching him as he talked. It was also a matter of pride. He just had to make good, especially after two others had failed. Maybe there was something I could do.

Late one afternoon I took the babies and went down to the store. Mr. Lykins, the proprietor, seemed a little friendlier — or, rather, less gruff — than he was before. I had hoped some of the women would be there, especially a Mrs. May whom I'd met once before. But no, Mr. Lykins was alone in the store, so I bought a box of oatmeal, " passed the time of day " with him, and returned home, feeling that I'd made a little headway in the interest of peace and good will.

I had gone to church — only it wasn't really a church, though it did have a cemetery in the yard. It was a school-house during the week, and on Sundays a preacher came over from Salyersville and held services. " Brother Bascom," as the minister was called, was as dull a talker as I ever heard, his sermons being impressive mainly for length. He'd had no training for the ministry — " just a call from God," he said, and I wondered if he hadn't misunderstood Him. After the service, Mrs. May had stepped over and spoken to me.

" Howdy, child," she'd said, smiling sort of shyly. " I been wantin' to come over and see you and your young-'uns. I'm Emmy Lou May."

She was a large, pleasant-looking woman in a black dress which hung, without benefit of curves, straight from her big-boned shoulders. I had a feeling that here, at last, was a friend.

" I'd love to have you come, Mrs. May," I smiled, and a feeling of warmth came over me. " You must be the Mrs. May whose husband works with Dux," I said. And, when she nodded: " He told Dux what wonderful gingerbread you make — even had him sample some. Maybe you'll show me how to make it sometime? "

" Well, I swan-to-David! " She threw up her hands, as if to deny the accomplishment, but looked highly pleased. " That old man o' mine would say anything — though I'd be right pleased to learn you."

We chatted a few minutes and I hurried home. Dux was

keeping the babies, and I knew he was anxious to get busy. No drilling was done on a Sunday, so that was the one day he had to study and work things out for himself.

The next day I had my first visitor in Ivyton, and a stranger visitor I have never seen. I was in the kitchen baking cookies while the babies napped, when I heard the front screen door squeak. Confident that no one but Dux would enter without knocking or calling " Hello," I ran to the living room door and looked in. Then I stopped dead in my tracks and my jaw must have dropped an inch.

Standing in the middle of the room, staring down at the floor, was a tall, thin woman whose high cheekbones only served to accentuate the gauntness of her weather-beaten face. She wore a gray calico Mother Hubbard dress, and was barefoot. Pushing her stringy gray hair back with a wrinkled, work-reddened hand, she looked around, caught sight of me, and jumped — as if I were the intruder.

" H-hello," I stammered, edging toward the door of the bedroom where my babies were sleeping. I recalled stories I'd heard of crazy people roaming about through the hills when they should be in institutions.

She looked at me with vacant eyes and grinned a tooth-less grin. Then she squatted down on the floor and ran a hand over the cheap matting rug. " I heared you had a kiv-erin' on your floor," she said, as if that explained every-thing. Having satisfied herself that the report was true, she got up, went across to our one overstuffed chair, and sat down gingerly.

" Nice day, isn't it? " I said, wondering what I should do. She looked harmless enough, but you never could tell. By this time I was standing directly in front of the chil-dren's bedroom door, ready to bar the way if it became necessary.

Again she grinned at me and started to bounce on the

chair. " First time I ever seen one that give, let alone set in it." Folding her hands in her laps, she continued to bounce up and down, up and down, like a fascinated child. Then she stood up and her eyes traveled around the room, as if she were trying to memorize its contents.

" I 'lowed I'd come and set awhile," she said. " Hit shore is right nice, ma'am."

" Thank you," I said, and somehow I wasn't afraid of her any longer. I thought of the bleak lives of some of these hill people, of all the little comforts so many of us are inclined to belittle or take for granted, and I could feel only pity for this strange woman.

" Wait," I called after her when she started out the door. " I just took a batch of cookies out of the oven."

She looked at me intently — a little suspiciously, I thought — then repeated her toothless grin and followed me into the kitchen. I motioned her to a chair, put some cookies on a plate, poured a glass of milk, and set them in front of her.

Her jaw dropped, just as mine had only a few minutes before. " For *me?* " she asked, regarding me with incredulous eyes.

" Why, of course."

I nodded and turned away, touched by her gratitude for what was only a small gesture of friendliness. Hungrily, she ate the cookies and drank the milk. When she'd picked up the last crumb, she rose and, without a word, walked back through the living room. I followed, not quite knowing what to do next. At the front door she turned, looked at me wonderingly, then made her way down the walk and out the gate toward the dusty road.

I never found out who she was, nor did I ever see her again. To this day she remains part of the mystery, the strangely intricate picture that was life in Ivyton.

13

IT WAS TOWARD the end of our second week in Ivyton that storm warnings began to appear on a presumably cloudless horizon. Lulled into a false sense of security because nothing untoward had happened, we were peacefully eating supper when there was a knock at the front door. It would be one of the workmen coming to talk to Dux, I supposed, wondering why they always had to pick mealtime for such confabs.

But when Dux came back to the table, there was an odd expression on his face. " Honey," he said abruptly, " wouldn't you like to go over to West Liberty and visit your mother for a few days? I could drive you there on Sunday."

" Who was that, Dux? " I felt goose-pimples rising on my arms and, when he did not answer at once, I exclaimed: " Something's wrong. I know it. What is it, Dux? "

Reluctantly, he pulled a piece of paper from his shirt pocket. " Now don't get excited, Shortie. It's probably nothing but — "

Jerking the paper from his fingers, I read the crudely printed words:

YOU AINT WANTED HERE. GIT OUT.

I felt the muscles at the back of my neck stiffen.

"M-maybe it's just a kid's prank," I said, but deep down, somehow, I knew it wasn't.

"Maybe." Dux took the note, tore it into tiny pieces, and dropped them into the ash tray on the table. "But, honey, don't you see that having you and the children here makes it harder for me?"

"Oh, Dux," I wailed, "if there's really danger, I'll send them to Mother. But please don't make *me* go! I couldn't bear it — not knowing — not being with you."

He shrugged, poured another cup of coffee, and groaned: "All right. I'm probably making a mountain out of a molehill anyway. Seth's been keeping me posted about what's going on, and he didn't say anything about this."

"I wish you hadn't torn that note up," I said. "I wish you'd shown it to him."

"Forget it, Shortie. We'll just ignore it and see what happens. Chances are it's only bluff."

Long after Dux was asleep that night, I lay awake remembering tales of bushwhacking. I thought of the time Bill Brooks stabbed Jet Pendleton on Main Street in broad daylight, in West Liberty. But that was a feud, I reminded myself, dating back to the days when old "Grandpa" Pendleton was nineteen and ran off with Lutie May Brooks, then deserted her. And so that was different.

It was hard to decide what to do, and I fell asleep wondering if I should send the babies to West Liberty and hire someone to help Mother look after them. I was certain of only one thing: *I* was staying with Dux; all the bushwhackers in Magoffin County couldn't drive me away, as long as he remained at Ivyton!

Nothing happened over the week end, and we began once more to relax. The threatening note, we decided, was either an ill-timed joke or a prank of youngsters. I didn't go to church that Sunday because Dux was busy and there was no one to keep the children — although most of the women took their babies and, to my surprise, even let them nurse during the service! It was a common occurrence for a nursing mother to bare her bosom and sit throughout the sermon, drinking in the minister's words, while her baby enjoyed all the privileges of a public milk bar.

Dux was anxious to get the pipeline started by Monday morning, so he spent Saturday and Sunday getting the pipe unloaded from a flatcar and hauled out to the job. This line would carry the gas from the wells to the main twelve-inch line about eighteen miles away. He worked early and late, eating his dinner and going straight to bed when he got home. But when he came home Monday night he was nervous and jumpy.

" Did you tell Seth about that note? " I asked, tentatively.

He shook his head. " Seth hasn't been to work since Friday — that's three days hand running. His boy Mike said he has a ' misery.' Sounds fishy to me."

He lighted a cigarette, leaned against the kitchen door, and smoked in silence for a moment. " I don't like the way the men are acting, either," he confided. " Nothing I can put my finger on — but they seem to be holding back on laying the line. They were good workers on the rigs."

" Maybe they're just tired," I said hopefully, sticking a knife into the pot roast and wiping the perspiration from my face on the corner of my apron. " It's pretty hot to be doing such heavy work."

" They're used to that. No," Dux said after a brief pause. " I've got a feeling there's something in the wind. I wish to heck you'd go to your mother's."

" For heaven's sake," I began, slamming the dish towel down on the table, " You know very well — "

" Oh, skip it, Shortie," he said wearily. " I don't want to

argue with you." He turned and walked toward the living room, leaving me to stew in my own juice, as the saying goes.

Hot tears stung my eyes as I started taking up supper. It was obvious that I could expect no encouragement from Dux in so far as my staying in Ivyton was concerned. Why, I couldn't even argue with him, now! It was an impasse, if ever there was one. I thought of Mrs. May, the only person I could talk to here, and made up my mind to see her the next day. I had a hunch that she would at least be frank with me, and maybe tell me what I should do and what the general feeling actually was.

Sometime during the night I awoke with a start, and the next moment I was sitting upright in bed, wide-awake, brought to sudden consciousness by a series of terrifying sounds. Dux was sitting up too. I clutched his arm and whispered, " What is it? "

It sounded, at first, like a bunch of Comanche Indians yelling at the kill. Then there was the unmistakable sound of a gun being fired, followed by a volley of shots. A kind of paralysis gripped me as I listened, but I managed to grab Dux's arm as he swung his feet to the floor.

" Don't! " I begged him. " Please don't go out there! "

He jerked away from me, muttering something about getting his gun and putting a stop to these goings on, whatever they were. I held my breath, fearing he would try to make good his threat. I knew about the gun; he had bought it in Louisville — for hunting purposes, he had assured me. I had no way of knowing then that he'd spent many hours perfecting his marksmanship, in the event of trouble at Ivyton. I flung myself upon him.

" You can't go out there, Dux," I sobbed. " I — I won't let you. There must be hundreds of them."

Then, just as suddenly as it had started, the weird din

stopped. In the quiet that followed, we could hear the sounds of horses' hoofs, and finally they faded away into a silence that was almost as frightening as the noise itself. Dux got up and lighted the lamp and we looked at each other incredulously. The whole incident seemed like a nightmare come true.

" Now what the hell did that mean? " Dux said angrily. " I'm going to see Seth and find out what's what. I'm damned if I put up with such shenanigans." He picked up a pack of cigarettes from the bedside table and I noticed that his hand was shaking.

Although it was only a little past midnight, neither of us felt like going back to sleep. I got up, closed the door to the children's room, marveling that they had slept through such noise, and went to the kitchen. Over coffee, Dux mentioned a scheme he had in mind, said he wanted to talk it over with Seth before putting it into effect, adding vaguely,

" If I can make the natives stop blaming us for what happened years ago — get them to trust me — our troubles will be over."

" Well, I don't blame them for being mad over losing their rights," I said, still shaking from fright. " But they've got no business shooting at *us!* "

" Maybe they weren't — really." Dux smoked thoughtfully. " Just trying to scare us. They've got us mixed up with a principle. I think I've got the whole thing doped out. They like to have the wells drilled — it gives them work and hopes for the future. But it burns them up to see the gas going out from them and the coal companies getting the royalties."

" They should take it to court," I said indignantly, " instead of taking it out on us."

" They tried that — Seth told me — and got nowhere.

So they fight with the only weapons they know — guns. Like wounded animals, they're apt to fight friend and foe alike," Dux pointed out. " And heaven help the innocent bystander. That's why I wanted you to go to your mother's — still do."

I smiled at him, then hastily changed the subject. Nothing — absolutely nothing — would send me away from him now.

He ate breakfast and left early in order to stop at Seth's house on his way to the job. I was in the kitchen making the baby's formula and Buddy was running a choo-choo at my feet, when I heard the back screen door open and looked around. I'd just started to open a can of powdered milk for the baby, and I threw the can opener down with a glad cry as Mrs. May walked in.

" I'd begun to think you'd forgotten your promise to come to see us," I said, pulling a chair out from the table and pushing scattered toys aside with my foot. " You're the very person I've been wanting to see. Do sit down."

" Lordy, but it's sure hot! " She sat down, pulled off her gingham sunbonnet, and began to fan herself.

" Yes — it is." I smiled at her and motioned to Buddy. " This is my little boy. Shake hands with Mrs. May, dear." Beaming with maternal pride, I watched as Buddy walked right up to her, put out his hand and said,

" Hi May." He pointed a small finger at the picture breastpin she was wearing. " Your lil boy? "

She leaned down and hugged him. " Yes, child — but he's gone now," she said simply. Then, to me: " Ain't he the smart young'un? With them gold curls, he oughta been a girl."

" Baby Sis has curls too," I announced proudly. " Auburn ringlets. She's asleep now, but I'll get her up before you have to go."

She stopped smiling and looked at me seriously. "Maybe I hadn't oughta come. Leastways Jeb — that's my ole man — says 'taint none o' my lookout, but fool men ain't got no sense nohow." She put her sunbonnet on the table and leaned toward me. "I heared about last night, and wanted you to know I don't hold with such goin's on. You musta been scared plumb out o' your wits."

"I was." I started to add that Dux was scared too, but thought better of it and said: "Do you know why they wanted to scare us? We've done them no harm."

When she didn't answer, I said: "I intended to come over to see you today. Will you tell me what I should do? Dux thinks I ought to take the children and go to Mother's, but — "

"You ain't goin' to do no such thing," she broke in spiritedly. "Your place is right here with your man. Me — I'm goin' to look after you; Jeb can just mind his own business." She stood up and put a protecting arm around me.

A lump came up into my throat and I pressed my head against her ample bosom, feeling peace and security surge through me. It was comforting, having a woman friend who saw eye to eye with me in a strange new world seemingly ruled by resentment and strife.

Despite repeated avowals that she had churning to do and butter to make, Mrs. May stayed for two hours. We talked for a while about woman-things and then, getting personal, she told me something about the people around Ivyton, with accent on the "menfolks" and their feeling against outsiders.

When Dux came home that night, I gave him quite an earful of local gossip. "Mrs. May knew all about the shooting and yelling last night," I told him. "She said those no-goods are running moonshine stills down the hollow from your wells and they're afraid you'll stumble onto them. They want to scare us away. Her brother," I raced on, " knew about it too — but he let them go ahead because he's mad about the pipeline. And — "

I stopped for breath, then picked up where I'd left off: " Mrs. May is so mad she's fit to be tied. Says she doesn't hold with such goings on. I told her about the threatening note and she just shook her head, said she sure was going to give that scamp of a brother of hers a piece of her mind. And — "

" Whoa — back up! " Dux laughed. " I've lost you. What's her brother got to do with it? "

" Oh — didn't I tell you? Well, he's the boss around here. Practically everyone does what he tells them to. Except Emmy Lou May." I grinned, remembering the woman's snapping brown eyes and her clenched fists.

" No, no, Shortie." Dux shook his head. " You've got it wrong. Hank Mullins is the boss — Seth said so."

" That's it," I said, exasperated. For a man as smart as Dux, he could be awfully dumb at times. " Hank's her brother."

Dux sat up straight and whistled. Then he grinned at me. " Now I get it — and she's on our side? "

I nodded. " And she's the sweetest thing, Dux. She stayed two hours and we talked. She thinks our babies are the smartest and prettiest she ever saw. She's only got a married daughter; both her boy babies died. I showed her our wedding pictures, told her all about how you built us a tent home — " I broke off and sighed, suddenly conscious of a faraway look in his eyes. " You haven't heard a word I said! "

His eyes were half closed and his forgotten cigarette was about to burn his fingers. " What — what, honey? " He grinned. " I was thinking about that scheme I mentioned to you." He got up and reached for his hat. " I'm going to run over and see Hank Mullins, make him a proposition. I'll be back by the time you get supper on the table."

He came back a little while later, wearing an expression not unlike that of a cat that has just raided a cream jar. " Well," he said as he sat down at the table, " there'll be no further performances like last night — I hope, I hope."

While we ate, he told me about a proposition he had made to Hank Mullins, the local kingpin. Feeling that the farmers had reason for grievance, he was offering, on behalf of the Gas Company, a reasonable sum for the gas taken off the various leases.

" Of course," he pointed out, " we're not obligated to do it — and I'm not sure the bigwigs will approve. But if they're going to say it with guns around here, seems we'll have to say it with money. Three hundred dollars for each well and free gas — that's what I'm offering — is little enough to pay for peace and good will. We've got problems enough without gunfire."

" Yes, I know. You don't have to tell me *that!* " I did not need to be told that laying a pipeline even under the most favorable conditions was no cinch. And here at Ivyton, because of the bad roads, it took a yoke of oxen a whole day to move a single joint from the railroad to the right of way! But I wanted to know more about Dux's confab with Hank Mullins.

" But what's Mullins got to do with it? " I asked. " I know he's supposed to be the local boss, and all that, but — "

Dux grinned. " That's just it, Shortie. I decided it's a good idea to have the boss man playing on our team," he said modestly.

So he had hired Hank to visit every farm where there was a gas well, he said. Hank was to find out if the owners

147

would be satisfied with the arrangement, and he was to be paid three hundred dollars a month, plus a dollar a day for his horse.

" He snapped the proposition up — just like that." Dux popped his fingers in illustration. " Thinks it'll work too. That should dispose of the landowner problem! " Then his expression became serious and he added:

" But we've still got the moonshiners to reckon with — though Mullins should be able to keep them in line too. He still feels I should carry a gun — just in case. And we're to keep a gun on the headache post out at the rig at all times. It's the one thing that seems to command a kind of wholesome respect in these parts."

14

A FEW DAYS LATER Hank Mullins, having made the rounds, reported fine progress. The local farmers had been so amenable to the idea that he felt free to take a little vacation and told Dux he was going into Salyersville that night — on personal business — confident that there would be no trouble while he was away.

That was the night when the telephone rang around nine o'clock, summoning Dux out to the wells. " Don't wait up for me," he said, as he picked up his gun and started to leave. " We've got a fishing job on hand and I may have to stay all night." He grinned when he saw that I was eying the gun a little apprehensively. " Don't worry, Shortie. It's just part of the sartorial equipment. Seems all well-dressed men around here wear firearms."

Shortly before dawn I was awakened by strange noises that I was sure came from our kitchen. I heard a chair topple over, a clatter of dishes, then Dux's voice muttering words that I preferred not to distinguish. It didn't make sense — Dux was not given to profanity of that sort — so I lighted the lamp, threw on my robe, and hurried to the kitchen to see what all the fuss was about.

Dux, a sorry figure if ever there was one, stood with the percolator in his hand, a broken cup and saucer at his feet.

Obviously, he had been trying to make coffee without lighting a lamp, not wanting to disturb me. I looked at him and laughed aloud.

"It's not funny," Dux snapped. "Damn it — you don't have to laugh!"

He was a sight! "A show for the dogs," Mrs. Dean would have said. He looked as though he'd been wallowing in the mud; his clothes were dripping wet, his pants torn, and his face was redder than I'd ever seen it before. Dux was not only a sorry sight to behold; he was hopping mad!

It was not until I had cleaned up the mess of broken dishes and he was drinking the hot coffee I'd made that he calmed down to the point where he could tell me what actually had happened.

The fishing job finished, he was returning home on Dixie, his spirited mare, riding along the creek bed, when he heard horses coming. As a precaution, he had pulled his gun half out of the holster and waited. Two men had passed him, but when they called a friendly, "Howdy," he'd relaxed.

"I'd no more than decided it was a false alarm," Dux went on to say, "when a bullet whizzed past my head. It scared Dixie worse than it did me, and she reared. I hadn't expected that. It came so suddenly that I — well, the next thing I knew I was down in the damn creek!"

I was all concern now. This was no laughing matter, I decided, though I was still reluctant to believe the men really intended to shoot Dux; they were just bluffing. Then I looked down and spied Dux's hat on a chair where he'd thrown it, saw the bullet hole, and my heart went cold. I scarcely heard the rest of the story; only the high spots stood out.

Dux, recovering himself, had shot into the darkness, and Dixie, thoroughly frightened, had gone wild, galloping off in the direction the two men had taken. Then he had emptied his gun, shooting wild, and walked home. Dixie had already arrived and was grazing contentedly out near the barn where the saddle horses were kept.

"Then I came in and made coffee — or tried to, at least," Dux admitted. "Didn't want to wake you — had no idea I'd make such a mess."

The next evening around dinnertime a sheepish and rather apologetic Hank Mullins paid us a surprise visit. Refusing Dux's invitation to come inside, he stood in the doorway, shifting his burly weight from one foot to the other and twisting his hat much in the manner of an embarrassed schoolboy.

"Mr. Gentry," he said to Dux, "I heared about last night. Emmy Lou — that's my sister — phoned me all the way to Salyersville. It was them dang moonshiners that done it."

"I thought so," Dux said. "At the same time — "

Before he could finish the sentence, Mullins cocked his head to one side, saying: "It ain't goin' to happen no more. They ain't goin' to bother you — none of us is. Us mountain folks may be ignorant an' mulish, but leastways we do know a man when we see one — and, by gum, we all aim to be friends."

Dux looked at him suspiciously. "What brought this on?" he asked.

Mullins looked at me, then at his hat in his hands. "Well," he drawled, "you're playin' pretty fair with the folks around here — "

"You knew that before the shooting last night."

"That's right." Mullins gave his hat another twist and leaned against the door facing. He seemed to be having some difficulty putting his thoughts into words. "What I was about to say — well, I been talkin' to Lafe Timmons, one o' the men that shot at you last night. Lafe runs a still down by the creek. Seein' as how you come from the city, him and his partner 'lowed as how you'd be scared an' maybe leave. But when you rode right *at* 'em, shootin' in the face of their bullets, they was mighty dang surprised."

" Rode *at* them? " Dux repeated, without thinking.

" Yep. They heared you comin', lickety-split. So they ain't goin' to bother you no more. Folks in these parts have got plenty of respect for a man who's got guts — beggin' your pardon, ma'am," the bad man of Magoffin County added, with an apologetic glance at me.

The two men shook hands and Mullins left. For several minutes Dux and I stood staring at each other, speechless. Then I got hysterical, didn't know if I was laughing or crying, till Dux shook some sense into me. We never did tell anybody that Dux wasn't on the horse that rode into the bullets, that the terrified animal was only hotfooting it home to the barn. But Dixie must have wondered why she got more oats than any of her barn mates!

After that, life in Ivyton settled down into a calm and rather pleasant routine. Dux built his pipelines without interference and, except for a few squawks from the accounting department at the head office, the consensus of opinion was that the general good will more than justified the extra cost to the company.

As for me — I began to like Ivyton, despite the isolation, the elemental way of life. It sent a glow of happiness through me to meet someone on the road and hear a friendly, " Howdy," to stop and chat about the weather, the crops, or the best way to put up sweet pickles. Nothing's more important than friends, I thought — except a husband and babies, of course.

I loved to visit with the women who came to shop at Mr. Lykins' store; to swap " receipts," as they called them, and talk about our respective children. Sometimes these conversations were so forthright as to be a little embarrassing, as in the case of one woman who confided:

" I'm goin' to make a lady out of my Sary Jane. She's ten now, but I aim to make her wear shoes, come summer." She leaned closer and whispered, " And I ain't never goin' to let her go 'thout her drawers."

Somewhat astonished, I whispered back, " Does anyone — ever? "

She laughed, as if I had made a good joke. " Lordy, Miz Gentry, why, I ain't never owned a pair! "

We spent a few days with the home folks in West Liberty and brought little Russell back with us to Ivyton. Mother's health, although improved, was still not too good. It was necessary for her to take frequent trips to Louisville for treatment, and the care of a lively youngster was too much for her. Drexel was away at school and Dad, of course, was busy. Frances, Mother's hired girl, came to help me with the children.

From where I sat there was only one serious drawback to life in Ivyton. The condition of the roads made it impossible to drive a car, and so the three babies and I were marooned. It was this situation that prompted Dux to buy a motorcycle with a sidecar the following spring. It created quite a sensation and, although it was faster and more modern than a horse, there were times when it took a horse to get us out of the mud!

I shall never forget the fiasco that our first ride turned out to be. Frances was to keep Baby Sis while Dux, the little boys, and I went for a visit with some friends a few miles down the road.

Thrilled at the thought of going visiting in such fine style, and wanting to impress our friends with the blond beauty of my two sturdy youngsters, I dressed Buddy and Russell in their Sunday best and brushed their curls till they shone. They looked lovely, I thought, as we stepped into the sidecar, and it pleased me immensely to realize that I had made their white summer suits myself. Even the two boys seemed to sense the importance of the occasion and behaved like little angels. I thought I looked rather nice too, in the blue-sashed white dotted Swiss I had made myself — rushing the season, perhaps — and, for once since my marriage, I wasn't pregnant.

It was fun riding along, smiling at the farmers who stopped plowing to stare at us as if we were denizens of another world, or climbed fences to get out of the way of the newfangled contraption we were riding in. Some had never seen a motorcycle before, and one with a fancy sidecar that would hold a woman and two children was quite a novelty. So bemused was I that it came as a shock to me when Dux said:

"Hold on, Shortie. I've got to hit this hard."

Glimpsing the big mudhole in front of us, I clutched the two babies to my breast and braced myself. Dux had a windshield in front of him, but there wasn't any on our side. "Maybe he doesn't realize this," I told myself, and opened my mouth to warn him. But the next instant he "hit it hard," and the unspoken warning was lost in a mouthful of mud!

Dux glanced at us and roared to a stop. The two children weren't blond and curly and white — not any more. They were covered with mud and screaming with rage. I wasn't much better!

Dux is above the average in lots of ways, but he seems to have a peculiar faculty for laughing at all the wrong times. He was still chuckling when we got home.

"You did it on purpose," I sputtered, and was instantly ashamed of myself. It could have been worse, I reflected. I could just as easily have married a grouch, a stranger to laughter. And the mudhole could, just as easily, have been a bottomless pit.

It took me hours to get the red, clayey mud out of our hair and it was weeks before we finally called on our friends. In fact, it was several days before I could ride in the sidecar with any degree of enjoyment.

Meanwhile Dux's work had continued to run along smoothly, and it was a vast relief to me to see him wrap his gun carefully, put it into a pair of old saddle pockets, and push it to the back of the top shelf of our closet. As the job progressed, he hired new men, among them a huge, belligerent-looking individual whom everyone called " Bull " Bircham. We didn't know whether he came by the name because of his size or if he really was a bully, but we'd heard plenty of rumors, and it was generally known that he had a propensity for getting roaring drunk on occasions.

" I don't listen to gossip," Dux said when one of the more garrulous workmen suggested he get rid of Bull. " I'd rather make up my own mind — and good drillers are hard to find." As for Bull's drinking — that was none of his business, Dux declared, as long as he didn't drink on the job. Most pipeliners liked to drink, he pointed out.

Bull's first overt offense in the community was to place several bullet holes through the sign in front of the general store. It was on a Sunday night and old Mr. Lykins had refused to open his store to the drunken would-be customer. We heard the shots, but thought little of them, for by this time we had become acclimated to promiscuous gunfire.

Several days later when Dux rode up to the rigs, he said he sensed trouble when he got close enough to see Bull leaning against the lazy bench. Bull was drunk, belligerently drunk. Dux walked onto the derrick floor and, in a quiet, controlled voice, told the man he was through.

" You can go to the bookkeeper and get your time," he

said in a tone that brooked no refusal.

Bull simply stared at him and grunted.

Dux turned to the tool-dresser. " Stand by till I locate another driller. I'll be back in an hour or so."

Bull's reaction was typical of the man. Spitting out an oath, he stalked off the derrick floor, drawing a gun from inside his shirt as he did so. " No pip-squeak is gonna fire me," he bellowed, and sent a bullet through the steam gauge.

Terrified, the tool-dresser leaped to the ground and sought safety under the derrick floor, while Dux — after a fleeting glance at the gun on the headache post — ran to the throttle, hoping to get the tools off bottom before the power gave out, otherwise sand might settle around them and they'd have to be fished out. But he was too late. In the confusion brought about by the escaping steam, Bull jumped on his mare, hitched to a nearby tree, and hurried away, shouting imprecations and threats as he went.

Dux came home thoroughly disgusted. He placed several long-distance calls, trying to find a driller to replace the discharged man. While he waited for them to come through, I made coffee and brought out some cookies. We were sitting at the kitchen table and he was telling what had happened, when there was a loud pounding on the front door. Pushing me aside, Dux went to investigate and I followed close behind him.

Bull Bircham, his face contorted with rage, stood swaying against the screen door. " I want my job back, you damned little squirt," he yelled, glaring at Dux with bloodshot eyes. " I'm gettin' it too. You just wait — "

The telephone rang and Dux slammed the door in the irate man's face. But Bull kept on shouting and, because the windows were open, his threats were clearly distinguishable. I gave Dux the telephone receiver and he held his hand over one ear, trying to hear above the noise outside. Suddenly the yelling stopped and I ran to window in time to see Bull go toward the barn. Dux threw the receiver toward the hook on the wall, missed it and left it dangling, grabbed his hat, and jerked open the door.

" Oh, don't go out there, Dux! " I made a grab for him, but he brushed me aside.

Helplessly, I watched him going toward Bull, who was now coming out of the barn. I knew Dux was furious, but I also knew that he was outmatched as to size; knew too that even though the man was a bully, a coward full of moonshine was something to reckon with. Running to the bedroom, I pushed a chair into the closet and climbed up to reach the top shelf. My shaking fingers finally opened the saddle pockets and closed over the butt of Dux's gun. It didn't occur to me that a gun would never have been put away loaded and that I, in this moment of desperation, must have looked for all the world like a heroine in what today is known as " soap opera." My only thought was that Dux was in danger, unarmed, and might be killed by that big drunken brute.

As I ran out the door, I caught a glimpse of Dux clutched in Bull's hairy arms. By now a crowd of men had gathered and I screamed, trying to push through them. Someone held my arm just as a yell of anguish broke from Bull.

" Git him off me! " he croaked. " He's killin' me! "

A loud guffaw came from the man next to me and a concerted snicker passed through the group. I stood there, staring, scarcely able to believe my ears. My eyes too seemed to be playing tricks.

Again, Bull gave out a mighty roar, his shaggy head thrown back. Dux stepped away from him, pulled a handkerchief from his pocket, wiped the perspiration from his face, and grinned as he reached for his hat on the ground. In a daze I watched Bull stumble to his horse, finally manage to mount, and someone slapped the animal on its rump. For some reason, I felt a little foolish as I hid the gun in my apron and hurried back to the house.

I was still torn between fright and bewilderment when Dux came in, though I tried to keep from showing it. " W-what happened? "

" Nothing much." He washed his hands in the kitchen sink, and dried them on my dish towel, ignoring the hand towel hanging on the wall.

" Don't tell me that! Bull's twice your size and I thought you'd be killed."

" Could be I outsmarted him — he won't be back soon," he said, a broad grin on his face. " New driller will get here tomorrow."

" But I want to *know!* " I demanded. " I don't understand! "

He made a gesture as if giving up and said, " All right, Shortie, if you must know, it was just a little jujitsu — there are certain parts of a man's anatomy that, when thoroughly squeezed, can make a yelping cur out of the biggest and brawniest brute."

" Oh," I said, and lapsed into a discreet silence.

15

THE IVYTON FIELD was nearing completion, but there was plenty of maintenance work to be done and I hoped the Gas Company would let Dux stay. In spite of the trouble we'd had at the start, Dux and I liked the people and hated to think of leaving. But we'd been there exactly seven months and two weeks when Mr. Addison telephoned that he was sending a man to take over the field and wanted Dux to be in Frankfort the following week.

The next Sunday Dux took the babies and me to Mother's and left for Frankfort early Monday morning. "You be ready in case I can send for you," he told me. " I'll call you as soon as I know what's up."

The night after he left I gathered up all our soiled clothes and took them to Mother's washwoman, to be ready to move on when Dux phoned. But that very night he called, saying I was to take the early morning train. " I don't have to work tomorrow," he explained. " I'll meet you in Lexington at noon."

After I put the children to bed, Mother and I washed and ironed the only clothes they had left. Mother promised to mail the other things, though she thought it was a little crazy of me not to wait one more day for them. But most of my relatives thought I was crazy anyhow.

Dux met us at the station in Lexington and we took a taxi to a small family hotel. We had lunch sent up to the room — an unholy luxury in those days, but Buddy had dribbed chocolate candy down the front of his suit and I couldn't take my babies into the dining room without clean clothes.

That afternoon, Dux played nursemaid while I went out and bought material and patterns and rented a sewing machine. Then I started stitching like the proverbial house afire. It was wonderful to get my spring sewing done in the hotel — no meals to get, no house to clean — and I made pretty good headway. But I did miss Mrs. Dean doing the buttonholes, and after several attempts at making the ghastly things I decided to put tiny flaps on Buddy's pants to hold a belt that would hide the safety pins.

Dux went back and forth to Frankfort every day. At that time there wasn't a good hotel in the capital city and the distance was only eighteen miles. There was a bill up in the legislature to stop the carbon-black people from wasting natural gas to make lead pencils, and Dux was there in the capacity of gas engineer. Actually, I guess, he was a lobbyist.

Mr. Erick came down from Chicago, and Dux got to know him quite well. He was one of the heads of the holding outfit that owned the Gas Company for which Dux worked, and was also stopping at our hotel. One night he invited us to dinner, urging us to bring the children along. That was when we met his wife, a partial invalid who had lost her only child in infancy and had never quite recovered from her grief. She seemed to enjoy being with our babies, and when I told her, a few days later, that we were going back to Mother's very soon, she looked disappointed.

" But — why? " she demanded. " Don't you like being here? "

" I love it! But we just can't afford it," I confessed. " We shouldn't have stayed this long — not really."

She looked so surprised that I wondered if she had any idea of the salary limitations of a struggling engineer. Then she smiled knowingly. " You just wait, my dear. Don't start packing yet."

That night when Dux came into the room he was wearing one of his broadest smiles. " What do you think Mr. Erick said today? "

" What? " I was poking oatmeal into my small daughter who took more interest in her daddy than she did in food, and kept reaching for him.

" He said I was to keep you and the kids here." Dux grinned and lifted the baby out of the chair into which I had tied her with a diaper. " Said I was to put you on the expense account and he'd O.K. it. Fine man, Mr. Erick."

Bless *Mrs.* Erick, I thought. It wouldn't have occurred to a man to do it.

It was wonderful living in the hotel without having to worry about the cost, and it gave me more time for sewing, for enjoying my children, and for training them. Baby Sis learned bathroom manners on the flowered spittoon that graced our room, just the right size for her fat little bottom. She learned to walk on the mezzanine floor, holding onto the spokes of the banisters. Buddy learned his ABC's from a book I'd bought at the ten-cent store, and he could count to twenty and recite several Mother Goose rhymes.

There was only one thing I didn't like about living at the hotel. The first time I carried Baby Sis into the dining room, Buddy trotting behind me, people looked at me and laughed. I didn't get the connection until a pompous-looking man stopped us and said:

" Where is Baby taking Mama? "

Baby Sis was big for her age, and had a quaint habit of

holding onto my ear. I must have weighed all of ninety pounds, and the short skirts in vogue then were no help. I guess we did look funny, but the remark made me so mad that I never again carried her into the dining room. If Dux or Mrs. Erick weren't there, we ate upstairs in our room.

Then there was the night when I grasped what I thought was opportunity by the forelock, believing I could help Dux in a really constructive way. The children and I had eaten our dinner and Mrs. Erick was telling Buddy a bed-time story. Baby Sis was asleep, so I went down to the mez-zanine to wait for Dux, who was having dinner with some men. I was sitting on a divan, leaning over the railing watching the people in the lobby, when a voice said:

" Hello — imagine finding you here! "

I looked up to see a man whom Dux had introduced as Senator Shoreham bending over me. He was one of the men Dux was having trouble trying to convince. He'd said time and again that this senator was against our bill and was next to impossible to talk to. Here is my chance, I thought.

" Why, good evening, Senator Shoreham," I said cor-dially. " How did things go in Frankfort today? "

He stood for a moment looking down at me, then came around to sit beside me on the couch. But he still hadn't answered my question, so I said, plunging in with both feet,

" Senator Shoreham, has it ever occurred to you that the amount of natural gas wasted on a little bitty old pencil would cook fifty meals for a family like ours? " I paused, trying to think what else Dux had told me on the subject.

Senator Shoreham laughed — a little strangely, I thought — and reached for my hand. " Don't bother your pretty little head about that. How about going down for a drink? "

Jerking my hand away, I said: " But it's important to

162

Dux — it's important to the Gas Company. The public too." He kept moving closer and I kept moving farther away until I was practically sitting on the arm of the couch. He's just a harmless old man, I told myself as I stood up in front of him.

"If you'll only look at it from a woman's angle — " I began again, determined to carry through with my crusade.

He grabbed my hand, almost pulling me onto his lap. "Listen, kiddo — "

"Winalee!" It was like the crack of a whip and I jumped. Dux was standing behind the couch, glaring at me. "Go upstairs," he ordered.

"But, honey, I was only — "

"Do as I tell you!"

With what dignity I could command, I walked toward the elevator. Dux didn't have to treat me like a child, I thought furiously, trying to keep from crying in the crowded elevator. When I got to our room, both the children were asleep and Mrs. Erick was waiting for me.

"I'm sorry. I didn't realize it was so late," I told her.

"That's all right. But you're crying, dear. What's the trouble?" She put her arms around me and patted my shoulder.

"It's Dux," I quavered. "He — he makes me so *mad!*"

The door burst open and Dux strode in. "Of all the asinine things I ever heard of!" he exploded. "This takes the cake!"

"But I was only trying to help — " I broke into sobs and Mrs. Erick's arms tightened around me.

"There, there, my dear," she tried to comfort me, then said to Dux, "Aren't you a little hard on her?"

"She ought to be spanked!" he shouted. "For crying out loud, Shortie, can't you tell when a man is drunk?"

"Senator Shoreham wasn't drunk," I said defiantly,

breaking away from Mrs. Erick.

" Senator Shoreham certainly *was* drunk! " Dux jammed his hands into his pants pockets and kicked at a chair. " So drunk he didn't care what he said."

" Well, how was I to know? He wasn't staggering," I said indignantly, and glanced at Mrs. Erick. A flicker of understanding mirth passed across her face, then was gone. I looked at Dux's flushed face and all the anger went out of me.

" I'm sorry." I ran over and pulled his head down, trying to make him kiss me. " I didn't know — I — I guess I'll stick to taking care of my family after this."

"That's right — *I'll* run the business." He kissed me lightly, a little reluctantly. Then his arms closed around me and we forgot Mrs. Erick until we heard the door close.

At the end of two months Dux's services were no longer required at the capital, and I began to wonder where we'd go next. Mr. Erick wanted some geological surveys made in an area near Lexington and, after a meeting with Mr. Addison, it was decided that Dux would remain to do the job.

" That means we'll probably be here five or six months," he told me, " so it's up to you to find us a furnished apartment."

While one of the hotel maids took care of Buddy and Baby Sis, I scoured the town for furnished rooms. But it was no use. Nobody wanted children. In exasperation one day, I squinted at a hard-boiled landlord and said in a stage whisper, " I'll chop off their heads, if you say so." He looked startled, then backed away from me and slammed the door.

Finally, we decided to rent a house and buy furniture. It was late one Saturday afternoon when we found a place. Then we rushed to a furniture store and bought stuff for five rooms — and it took us five years to pay for it! In a way, it was satisfying to have a house full of furniture, though most of it I'd never have chosen if given more time. When the furniture was in place, the curtains hung, everything spick-and-span, we relaxed and looked around, but there wasn't quite the glow of achievement that our tent home had given us. And, in spite of a brand-new stove, our first dinner didn't taste any better than the dinners I cooked in my tent kitchen.

Dux usually got home around five thirty. I'd feed the children early and have them ready for bed by that time, so he could romp with them and tell bedtime stories before we had dinner. One night he didn't get home until after seven. I was frantic and getting ready to send out an alarm when he arrived, his arms full of packages and a little-boy grin on his face.

" What have you been up to now? " I demanded.

For answer, he laid the packages carefully on the living room couch, tore off the wrappings, and held up a radio set, complete with two headphones. " I've been saving weeks for this," he gloated.

" Oh, golly, Dux, that's wonderful! " I clapped my hands in delight. " If you'll get the kids to bed, I'll put dinner on the table — so after we eat we can hook it up! " Shooing the children into their room, I ran to the kitchen. Radios weren't so plentiful in those days; this was our first, and I was eager to get the thing going.

After dinner I left the dishes and we set up the card table. Dux strung wires every which way and both of us were in a fever of excitement over our new possession. Finally, everything in order, he turned the radio on, and we adjusted our headphones and settled down for what we believed would be a delightful evening of entertainment.

At first it was a little disappointing. Through the earphones came strange noises, as if a group of tone-deaf youngsters were pounding on tin pans. But presently we could hear music — or was it only a bunch of pranksters blowing through paper on combs? Just as the music began to get believable I looked up to see a man peering through the glass curtain of our front window. Removing the earphones, I got up and opened the door.

"Oh, Dr. Heizer," I said, recognizing our next-door neighbor. "Come in. I didn't hear the bell."

He nodded to me and said to Dux: "So you did get that radio set, Gentry! Mind if I listen awhile?"

Reluctantly, I gave him my headset. There was nothing else to do. For a few minutes I sat there, feeling very much left out. Then I went to the kitchen to do the dishes, wishing our neighbor would go home.

About twenty minutes later I returned to the living room. Dux and Dr. Heizer, wearing the two headsets, sat facing each other, laughing and nodding at intervals. It was clear that Dr. Heizer had no intention of going home any time soon.

I sat down in Dux's lap and leaned my ear over against the headset, but I couldn't hear a thing — at least not from the radio. All I heard was a wail from the children's bedroom, "Mommy, I want a dink of water."

I got the water for Buddy and another glass for Baby Sis, who had wakened and put in her order. By that time I was so mad I threatened to spank both of them if they didn't go right to sleep, and went back to glower at the two men in the living room.

Dux pulled the phones off his head. "Here, honey, you listen." I took them, adjusted them on my head, but this time all I heard was, "That right to the jaw was terrific . . ."

I appealed to Dux. " I don't want to hear an old fight. Can't you get some music? "

Dux made a motion toward our visitor and shook his head. I flung the headphones down and went to bed.

" I'm sorry, Shortie," Dux said the next morning. " I told Dr. Heizer yesterday I intended to get the set and he wanted to hear the fight. But tonight we'll have it all to ourselves."

He got home early and we hurried through dinner, rushed the bewildered children off to bed, and got our headsets adjusted in time for the first program. It was wonderful, though a little noisy. We're making history, I thought. Someday I can tell my grandchildren we had the first radio in our neighborhood. . . .

I felt Dux punch me and looked around as he jerked his head toward the front door. Through the glass I saw Ed Wilson, another neighbor, and groaned aloud. I wondered how long he'd been standing there and wished I didn't have to let him in. With a sigh of resignation, I put the headset on the card table and opened the door.

" Hi," Ed Wilson said, brushing past me. Without so much as a by-your-leave, he made a beeline for the table, put on my headset, grinned at Dux, and sat down.

For a full fifteen minutes I sat in stony silence, waiting for Ed to leave. Dux, a pained expression on his face, motioned to his set, but I shook my head. Finally, in disgust, I went to bed. History, it seemed, was repeating itself.

The next morning I put breakfast on the table in grim silence. Dux came into the kitchen, leaned down, and kissed me. " Honey, we'll move everything into the bedroom tonight — so they can't see us through the front door. I'm sorry," he said, pouring the coffee.

" It's all right," I answered coldly. " If radio's an invention for men only, I guess I can take it."

We did move the card table, radio and everything, into the bedroom that night, turning out the living room lights in the hope that neighbors would think we weren't home. We had no more than settled down to listen to the music — at least I was sure it would be music once Dux got the static tuned out — when Buddy padded in.

" You didn't hear the bell, Mommy, so I opened the door," he said, and backed down the hall as Ed Wilson, his father-in-law, Dr. Heizer, and his wife, Betty Jean, trooped into the bedroom.

" Hi, folks," Ed said. " We knew you were home because the car's out front. How come you moved it in here? " he added, pointing to the radio.

The table with all the paraphernalia was moved back into the living room. Betty Jean and I played double solitaire while the men took turns with the headsets. Then we fixed coffee and cinnamon toast. It was midnight before our guests left and Dux and I got to bed.

" I can remember the nights when we could sit down, have a game of chess, or talk things over — " I began, when the lights were finally turned out.

" I know, honey — it's a shame. For two cents — "

" Yes, I know. For two cents you'd throw it out the window. You've said that before. But you scrimped for weeks to get it. What *are* we going to do?"

He didn't answer for a moment. " I've got it! " he exclaimed, switching on the bed light. " Tonight I'll put the car in the garage. We'll turn out every light in the house and listen in the dark. We'll lock the front door, and if the bell rings — "

" We'll just let it ring," I finished.

And that's the only way I got to listen to the radio, in those all-but-forgotten days when radio was young and television still a gleam in the inventor's eye.

16

BY THE END OF OCTOBER, Dux had finished the geological surveys in eastern Kentucky, completed his report on the reserves of natural gas and oil in that area, and mailed it to the head office. A few days later Mr. Addison telephoned and Dux left for Louisville, promising to call when he found out what our next move would be.

I was not surprised when he phoned me the following night and said to notify the landlord that we were giving up the house and to start packing. Sudden moves were no longer a novelty to me and, despite a growing family, I had learned to take packing and unpacking in stride.

It pleased me to hear that our next home — however temporary it might be — would be Louisville. I had many friends there, dating back to my girlhood, and I looked forward to renewing old ties as well as enjoying the companionship of Dux's friends and co-workers and their wives. It was a step up for Dux too. He was made superintendent of gas transportation for the Gas Company in addition to retaining his post as geological engineer. He also got a slight raise, which would help pay for the new baby I was expecting in January as well as provide a little more leeway for the family budget. He would come for us, he said, as soon as he could find a place for us to live.

The apartment Dux found was a lower duplex on First Street. " Like it? " he said anxiously, when I came to inspect the rooms. " I didn't have much time, of course, and the rent is a little more than I'd figured. But I thought the kids would enjoy the yard, and being on the ground floor would make it easier for you."

" It's fine, honey," I nodded, trying not to show my disappointment. I had wanted a house — but the living room did have a big fireplace, the back yard was fenced in, and there were golden chrysanthemums beside the door. " I'll love it," I said hastily, realizing that the advantages more than outnumbered whatever shortcomings the apartment might have.

Most of Dux's work was within driving distance of the city. This meant that he was home nearly every night, but he had started another correspondence course and spent practically all his waking hours with his books. It was also about this time that he met Dean Brown, head of a cooperative college in Louisville, where the boys were permitted to gain experience and earn while they learned. Dux gave jobs to some of the engineering students and Dean Brown was deeply interested in the practical side of the picture.

One day Dux came home wearing a smile that didn't come off even when he kissed me. " What do you know? " he said. " Dean Brown called me at the office, asked me to give a talk at the college. Wants me to explain some short cuts."

" Dean Brown's a smart man." I beamed with pride. " He recognizes brains."

Dux's grin faded. " Look, Shortie — it's gratifying to a practical engineer to be asked to talk to *college* students. But, hell's bells, I can't do that. No point in kidding myself."

" You won't be kidding yourself, and you know it! " I exclaimed. " You've got *more* than the equivalent of a college education — and you've got common sense to boot! "

" That's what Brown said," he admitted. " Maybe I have shown them some surveying stunts that are more practical than their theories. But I still can't see myself running off at the mouth in front of a college group — "

" *I* can," I said firmly. " And you'll come through with flying colors."

A week later Dux made his first public talk. He must have done a good job, for that talk was only the first of a series. But even today Dux is more likely to speak in actions than in words.

Mother, Dad, and Drexel came to see us at Christmas time and took Russell home with them. Mother was much better, walking now with a brace. She wanted to stay until after my baby came, but she wasn't strong enough to be much help. And, too, there wasn't room for both her and Mrs. Eastlin, the woman we'd engaged to look after Buddy and Baby Sis while I was in the hospital.

For weeks we'd been trying to think of a name good enough for a boy. " We're all set, if it's a girl," Dux pointed out.

" Yes — Harriet Virginia." I smiled. " Harriet for my mother and Virginia for yours. We'll have to start calling Baby Sis by her right name — Winalee — or maybe Lee, for short — if it's a girl."

We were in the living room and Dux was stretched out on the sofa in front of the fire. I was sitting uncomfortably erect on a dining room chair, holding the dictionary open at " proper names," against my bulging stomach. Every once in a while a swift kick would almost knock the book from my hands. Earlier in the evening I'd had a sudden craving for fresh peaches and, without a word, Dux got his hat and coat. Then I'd decided I didn't want peaches after all — so we were trying to settle the matter of a name for a son.

" What about Gilbert? " I looked up from the dictionary. " Gilbert Gentry — that's not bad."

Dux made a sour face. " They'd call him Gillie. No, I don't like it."

" Well," I read on, " Harold, Henry, Herbert, Hobart, Irwin — "

" Let's name him Jim, or Bill, or Tom. Good old American names." Dux yawned. " You know, I should have made that trip to Lexington today," he said, changing the subject.

" That's right. I told you to go ahead. A watched baby never comes — or didn't you know? " I misquoted the old saying. " Why don't you go tomorrow, get it over with? "

The business trip in question — Mr. Addison wanted him to look at a pumping station — had been scheduled for days. But Dux, knowing that my time was so near, had been waiting around, unwilling to leave.

" Guess I'd better go tomorrow," he said. " Addison asked me about it today. He's sympathetic, of course, but he feels the show must go on — baby or no baby. And I won't be gone long."

The next day he came home at noon and said: " I'm going now, honey; I hope to heaven it doesn't start till I get back. You know where to reach me. Laura Best is coming over to stay with you; Bob's going with me."

" Dux," I said when he'd kissed me good-by, " if I do have to call you, promise me you won't drive too fast. Cross your heart."

He grinned, crossed his heart. " Not over thirty-five miles an hour, baby. I promise."

I followed him to the door and waved to Bob Best, who

was sitting in the car, waiting. He worked in the engineering department with Dux and he and Laura, his wife, often came over for a game of bridge, or just to visit. They didn't have any children and she liked to be with ours. Laura would be a big help, I thought, in case anything happened. Because of the expense, Mrs. Eastlin was not to be summoned until my time came.

As it turned out, I made all arrangements, went to the hospital, and had my baby alone, except for Dr. Speidel and the nurses, but I was too busy to mind. Dux hadn't been gone three hours when the pains started, and Laura began wringing her hands.

" What'll I do — oh, what'll I *do?* " she wailed.

I guess she thought I was going to have it right there that minute. " You can call Mrs. Eastlin," I told her. " Then phone the doctor — the number's on a pad by the telephone — and get me a cab."

But by this time she couldn't even talk and her face had gone white — one would think that she was having the baby! When I laughed at her she stared at me, as if I'd lost my mind.

Between pains, I managed to get Mrs. Eastlin on the wire, then called the doctor and the hospital and ordered a taxi. My bag had been packed for a week. I wrote the telephone number down so that Laura could call Dux, when and if she recovered, and gave her a few instructions about the children, though I doubt if she heard them. Then the taxi came and I threw my coat around my shoulders, kissed Buddy and Baby Sis, and went out into the cold January day.

Harriet Virginia Gentry, later to be called " Ginger " by her doting parents, was born about ten minutes before her father got to the hospital. " The hardest thing I ever did in my life," he said, " was to hold that car down to thirty-five miles an hour. That's a snail's pace, honey, when a fellow's having a baby."

"*I* was having the baby, darling," I corrected him, and thought of Laura Best's crazy carryings-on.

"Same thing," Dux announced solemnly. "I wanted to drive faster — but I knew dang well if I broke a promise to you there'd be trouble of some kind."

When the baby was ten days old, I was allowed to walk down the hospital corridor, and was standing by a window when I overheard two nurses talking.

"Her little girl is terribly sick," one was saying.

"Yes — so I've heard," said the other. "They've engaged a private nurse. It's a pity too — the poor thing here in the hospital with a ten-day-old baby and — " She turned and saw me, put a finger to her lips, and the two of them hurried away, going in opposite directions.

I knew without being told that they'd been talking about Baby Sis, and my heart all but stopped beating. I found a telephone booth in the corridor and called Dux, but he wasn't in his office. Somehow I didn't dare call the house. Just then I saw Dr. Speidel and followed him to my room. He answered my questions with an evasiveness that alarmed me all the more. Finally, in desperation, I cried out:

"You're not fooling me. I *know* it's Baby Sis. If you don't let me go home, I — I'll walk right out of here in — in my nightgown!"

"All right, all right," he grumbled. "I'll let you go home — but you've got to be careful. Your child's probably got the flu — there's a lot of it around."

But it wasn't flu. It was pneumonia. Dux had a special nurse with her, but she'd been crying for me for days. When the worst was over, the crisis past, I insisted on letting the nurse go. Keeping her was a terrible expense and Mrs. Eastlin, who had been like a mother to the children during my absence, was more help. I spent hour after hour rocking Lee — as we called her now — to keep her quiet and relaxed, but it was weeks before she was entirely well.

Dux stayed at home a part of the time. For one thing, there was no janitor on the premises and it took a man to shovel coal into the furnace. Complaints to the landlord netted nothing more than vague assurances that he was doing the best he could to find someone to tend the furnace.

" Why don't we break the lease and find a house? " I said to Dux one day when the unhappy situation began to show signs of going on indefinitely. Mrs. Addison had told me about a house that was for sale in her neighborhood. I passed the information on to Dux. " It's a darling place with three bedrooms," I added. " Oh, honey, why don't we buy it? "

" I don't think that's the smart thing to do," he said. " We don't know how long we'll be in any one place."

" But you've just been made head of your department," I argued. " Doesn't that mean we can put down roots? You certainly can't do that in an apartment. Besides, we can afford it now, with your last raise — after we get the doctor bills paid."

" In other words, you want a house pretty bad, don't you, Shortie? "

" Oh, I'd love it, Dux. Buddy'll soon be ready for school, and I want us to be solid citizens before that happens."

I knew I'd won and, after Dux left for the office, I called Mrs. Addison. We must have talked on the phone for fifteen minutes. The next day was Saturday and Dux drove me out to see the place, stopping first at the Addisons' to leave the children. I was enthralled at the very sight of the house. It looked terribly expensive, but, as it turned out, the asking price just cleared our uppermost limit.

" My home," I breathed. " Number Eleven Eastover

Court! I never dreamed I'd own a house in what used to be the lane of the Little Colonel! "

I guess no one was ever more proud of a home than we were. It was like a long-cherished dream come true. On the day Dux made the down payment a group of my old friends gave a small bridge party and I could talk about nothing else.

" Of course there's a lot to do to it," I confessed, " but I'm so thrilled I have to pinch myself now and then to make sure it's me. Our first house that's really *ours!*

" Next week we're moving in," I gushed on. " Dux plans to concrete the garage. There's a lot of painting to be done, but we'll do it ourselves. And I'd like to tile the bathroom — if we can afford it."

" We'll have to get the crowd together and throw some work parties," one of the girls suggested. " They are fun."

And they were fun. The husbands went in together and bought a lot of bathroom tile wholesale. On Saturdays and Sundays they worked, doing everything together, while we wives fixed food, looked after the children, and ran errands. Thus, in the good old Southern tradition, several homes, including ours, got new tiled bathrooms or new paint jobs at the cost of only the materials. And Dux and I, in our new role of householders, became part of a happy community life that I'd missed more than I cared to admit.

We took footprints of our children and our friends' children in the wet concrete of the garage. We signed our names, wrote verses with nails, until the floor looked like a jigsaw puzzle gone haywire.

About that time one of Dux's secret dreams began to show signs of fulfillment. He had always loved boats, of any shape, form, or fashion. We were entertaining the Addisons at dinner one night when Mr. Addison announced in a casual voice:

" By the way, Dux, I put your name up for membership in the boat club. We need men who know how to sail."

Dux's quick smile did not escape me, nor did the half-regretful look that followed. " I — well, I'll have to think it over."

I knew he wouldn't like my saying it, but the truth slipped out. " We can't afford it, Mr. Addison. We're paying on the furniture, the car, and now the house. Why, we can't even afford to have the children's tonsils out," I blurted.

Mr. Addison threw up his hands. " All right, all right, I'll see that you get a raise, Dux. You deserve more than you're getting anyhow." He grinned at me. " That is, if you'll let him join the boat club, Miss Fixit."

Dux did join the boat club. But he was so busy working and studying that he didn't get to the river nearly as often as he would have liked. In spite of the small salary increase, rising expenses continued to harass us to the point that we kept putting off the tonsil operations. The doctor had assured us that there would be no harm in waiting a little while.

Then one night Lee woke up crying with a sore throat and we called the doctor. After he had quieted her, he said, " Those tonsils will have to come out before cold weather, or she's in for trouble."

Accordingly, a date was set and, since Buddy and Russell had bad tonsils too, we decided to have the operations done wholesale. Dad and Mother drove down with Russell and the mass tonsillectomies were on.

The three children were put in a large room at St. Anthony's and I was allowed to stay with them. When a doctor came to make the blood tests, taking a drop or so from each toe, Lee yelled to high heaven. She was still quite unhappy when Dux came in later.

"Look, Daddy," she sobbed, holding up her big toe for inspection. "They tooked out my tonsils."

The operations began a short time later, at eight o'clock in the morning — first Lee, then Russell, then Buddy. By afternoon the beds were strewn with toys and three heroic youngsters were gingerly sipping chocolate milk through straws. Dux and I were the only casualties.

17

WITH MORE ENTHUSIASM than strength, I worked day after day on our new home. Dux wielded a paintbrush at night and on week ends. Already the upstairs woodwork gleamed white, and he'd told me to make up my mind about the color for the kitchen walls.

One Friday evening the dinner was cooking on the stove and I was standing on a chair pushing the rod through the new kitchen curtains I'd just finished making, when Dux came in the back door.

" Hi," I said, surprised that time had slipped up on me. I look like the dickens, I thought, remembering Miss Abby's rule that a wife should be " prettied up " by the time her husband came home. But for some reason it didn't seem to matter now. I didn't feel well at all, but I supposed it was because of the new baby, and I probably needed more rest.

" Hi, yourself," he said. " You look tired, honey. Did you get a nap this afternoon? "

I pushed the hair back from my face and winced. That pain again — every time I moved. My chest hurt too and it was hard to breathe. " No," I said crossly. " Of course I didn't get a nap. How can I — the children underfoot, the baby, and so much to do? "

He stood watching a moment, then went on through the back hall into the living room, where the children were playing. I yanked the curtain over the end of the rod, hooked it up, and got down. He didn't even kiss me, I thought. That's what I get for looking so haggy. I jabbed a fork into the pot roast, turned the flame down under the potatoes, and looked at the peas. Dux came in and stood beside me. " What does it take to get a kiss? " he asked, putting his hand on my shoulder.

I turned and pushed him away. "You went right through the kitchen," I accused. "Didn't even stop."

He gave my cheek a pat and started back through the hall. "You were busy," he said. "I didn't think you wanted me to kiss you."

"I always want you to kiss me," I shouted, following him into the living room.

He pulled me down into a chair with him and kissed me. "What's wrong, honey? "

"N-nothing," I faltered, trying not to cry. "I'm just tired, I guess." It was heavenly to relax in his arms. Then I sniffed the air and jumped up. "My peas! " I cried, and ran into the kitchen.

How stupid, I thought, emptying the scorched peas and running cold water into the pan. Everything seems to be such a chore — it's not fun any more. I grabbed my side as another searing pain shot down my shoulder.

"Get the children and come on," I called to Dux, putting the dinner onto the kitchen table. Another bad habit — eating in the kitchen — I thought. But it was so much easier than carrying everything into the dining room.

The children trooped through the hall with Dux and I heard Buddy's loud whisper: " Better put your kid gloves on, Daddy. Mommy's on her high horse." It made me want to cry. Had I been mean to my babies, I wondered, and tried not to see Dux's grin as he lifted Lee into her high chair. Resentfully, I recalled Buddy's question only a few days ago, " You said mommies have to be handled with gloves. What does that mean, Daddy? "

Dux wiped the dishes for me and put the children to bed while I gave Baby Ginger her bottle. Holding her in my arms, I looked down at her, thinking how irresistible she was, and hugged her close. She stopped pulling on the nipple, looked up at me, and smiled. Tomorrow, I resolved, I'll let the house go, take a nap as I should, and pay more attention to my family.

After she was snug in bed, I went downstairs and saw that Dux had started to paint the back hall. " Why don't you paint the kitchen tonight? " I asked, a little sharply.

" I want to get this finished first. Then I'll be through with the white paint. I'll do your kitchen tomorrow."

" But I don't want it done on a Saturday." My voice rose, but I seemed unable to do anything about it. " I want it done *tonight!* " I tacked on defiantly.

Dux peered up at me from the basement steps. " Are you sick? "

" No," I whimpered.

" You certainly sound sick," he said. " Why don't you run on to bed and get some sleep? "

The very patience with which he spoke the words seemed to rouse every ounce of perversity within me and I heard myself shouting: " I'm not sick and I'm not going to bed. I want my kitchen painted *now!* " Oh, why couldn't he understand that the smell of paint and turpentine made me sick? Didn't he know I had baking to do on Saturday?

He turned and stared at me, paintbrush in one hand, a blotchy rag in the other. " Look, Shortie," he said softly, " if you don't like what I'm doing, get the heck away from me."

A searing rage blasted through me. " Oh — oh, you make me so *mad!* " A small bucket of water that he'd been using to wash the woodwork before painting stood at my feet. Suddenly, without thought, I gave the bucket a kick that sent it hurtling down the steps, splashing soapy water on the walls, on the newly painted woodwork, and on the big electric light bulb that Dux was using. It broke into smithereens.

For a second I stared unbelievingly at what I had done. My temples throbbed and I felt sick. Then I turned, ran upstairs, and flung myself across the bed, burying my face in the pillows.

How can you be so mean when you love him so much, my conscience nagged. It wasn't *all* my fault, I fumed, in self-defense. He made me do it. He's the one who should be sorry!

I lay with my eyes closed for what seemed like a long time, waiting for Dux to come upstairs, take me in his arms, kiss me, and tell me how sorry he was. Then it dawned on me that he wasn't coming and the sick feeling inside me grew sharper than ever.

Finally, I tiptoed down the stairs, peeked around the corner — but he wasn't there. I opened the door into the kitchen, and my breath caught in my throat. Dux sat on a stool in the middle of the floor, with his foot in an old dishpan and a blood-soaked rag in his hand.

" Oh, honey," I cried, " you're hurt — what happened? "

He just looked at me, a white line around his mouth. Then he muttered, " You're asking *me?* "

My eyes stung and I felt remorse. " I didn't — I mean, you weren't — was it glass from the light bulb? "

" No," he said shortly. " I cleaned up that mess, took it to the back porch, and stepped on a damned oilcan. Ran it through my bedroom slipper, probably a couple of inches into my foot. Why the hell can't you keep things in place? "

I remembered that Buddy, early that afternoon, had watched me oil my sewing machine. Intrigued by the tiny oilcan, he had taken it out to the porch, saying something about " doctoring " the wheels of his tricycle. Obviously he had left it right where he'd used it.

" Oh, darling," I said contritely, dropping to my knees, " your poor foot — let me fix it."

I poured in more hot water from the teakettle on the floor, dumped in more Epsom salts, and ran to the bathroom for bandages. The next morning I went with Dux to the doctor and gritted my teeth while I watched him probe into the ugly cut. I'm sure it hurt me as much as it did Dux — but I felt I deserved the punishment.

When we were about to leave, the doctor motioned to me. " Come here," he said. " Stick out your tongue — I don't like the way you look."

" Oh, I'm all right," I said.

But he made me sit down and he listened to my chest with his stethoscope, took my temperature, and looked down my throat.

" You go straight home and get into bed, young lady," he ordered, putting little pink pills into a small envelope. " And take these as directed. I'll drop in to see you tomorrow. You've got a nasty case of bronchitis, and," he added ominously, " we don't want you curling up with pleurisy too."

For two weeks thereafter I was out of circulation, in so far as work on our new home was concerned. Mrs. Eastlin took over and I had plenty of time for reflection over past mistakes — plenty of time to make plans for the future. Dux felt that we should take a vacation, so we decided on Carolina Beach, and as soon as I could I began to plan and

183

to lay aside money for the anticipated trip.

Meanwhile, Dux worked every Saturday and Sunday on our house, making it more comfortable to live in. But his interest seemed to begin with the house and end with the garage. No matter how much I cajoled, he wouldn't do one thing for the yard. I had learned a lot about flowers and spent many hours digging, pruning, and transplanting. But I couldn't make the grass live up to the velvet-green lawns of our neighbors and I was ripe for suggestions when a man came to the door one day and said:

"How about sellin' you some manure, lady? Your grass sure needs it."

There was no denying that it needed something more than wishful thinking. "Will manure make it thick and green — like Mrs. Bowman's? " I asked, pointing to the attractive lawn across the street.

"Sure thing. Grass needs food. And I do all the yards in this neighborhood."

I was impressed, but dutifully budget-conscious. So I asked, cautiously, "What do you charge? "

"The usual rate, ma'am," he answered. "Dollar and a half a yard."

That sounded reasonable enough. "All right," I told him, "go ahead. Spread it on thick and don't miss the edges."

I went back to my sewing and he started unloading. He was still spreading the smelly brown stuff when Dux came home from the office.

"What the heck goes on? " he greeted me, holding his nose.

"He's feeding our grass," I announced smugly. "Our grass needs food, he says. He does all the yards in this neighborhood."

"From the smell of that stuff, I think it'll founder,"

184

Dux said, grinning. " I hope you know what you're doing, Shortie."

" Certainly I know what I'm doing," I announced loftily, then broke off to say, " Did you write Carolina Beach about getting a cottage? " It pleased me to realize that we had over a hundred dollars in a special savings fund, making our vacation at the seashore an assured thing.

" Glad you reminded me," Dux said. " I'll do it tomorrow, first thing."

I sliced some country ham and put it on to cook — it surely smelled better than the air outside. About that time someone knocked on the door and Dux went to see who it was. He came back with a queer expression on his face.

" Your manure man says you owe him seventy-nine dollars," he said.

" I do not," I gasped. " Only a dollar and a half. He said so. A dollar and a half a yard," I repeated, for emphasis.

Dux looked at me in exasperation, shook his head, and left the kitchen.

" I gave your man a check! " he said when he came back, regarding me with accusing eyes. " Tomorrow you can march down to the bank and draw out your savings to cover it."

" But that's our *vacation* money," I wailed.

" There'll be no vacation *this* year, Shortie," he said firmly. " But after this, you'll know the difference between a cubic yard and a front yard."

Being Dux, he laughed about it later, but I knew very well I was in the doghouse for the time being. We spent our " vacation " at home, and I didn't feel any glow of pride that summer when our neighbors spoke of our beautiful lawn!

18

AFTER THE OHIO RIVER CROSSING, when Dux had taken the bull by the horns and laid the pipeline without benefit of authority, officials of the Gas Company seemed to have more respect for his ability. At least, they gave him more responsibility, with a small raise. Not nearly enough, I thought, and Dean Brown, impressed by Dux's helpfulness with his students, agreed with me.

But money didn't seem to mean much to Dux, so long as we had enough to get by on. And it didn't even seem to matter to him when, occasionally, someone else got credit for the work he did. It did matter to me and I often sputtered about it, asking him why he didn't leave the Gas Company. He'd had several interesting offers. But he liked his work and he had the highest regard for Mr. Addison and Mr. Lewis.

" Maybe someday I'll make a change, Shortie," he would say. " But right now I'm getting education and experience. Those are things no one can take away from me. Besides, we've got a home here, and we're settled."

It was wonderful to be settled, I had to admit. Our roots were down; we were solid citizens and, for the first time since our marriage, we had a little social life — going to church affairs, boat club parties, and playing bridge. That is, we did on week ends when Dux didn't have extra work. During week nights he continued to study.

The first Christmas in our own home — that is, one that was really a house — we'll never forget. Mother and Father Gentry came from New York, and my folks met them for the first time. For three weeks ahead of time I was in a dither — shopping, planning, cleaning, getting everything in readiness, for I wanted this gala occasion to be perfect. It was my first really big dinner, and I cooked it myself — from the turkey straight through to the luscious pumpkin pies.

I loved the gay city streets, the tinsel and glitter of the store windows, the brightly wrapped packages and gifts on display, the hurrying crowds, the Salvation Army Santas standing on corners ringing their bells. The joyous spirit of Christmas was everywhere. It was in my heart too, for we were going to have the happiest Christmas of all!

We made a holly wreath, gay with shiny leaves, bright red berries, and a huge red ribbon bow, and hung it on our front door. We decorated the dining room with fir and holly and mistletoe and I made a centerpiece of green stuff with gilded walnut shells and pine cones. Dux set up the tree in front of the living room window, and Buddy and Lee helped us trim it with popcorn and cranberries we'd strung ourselves, gleaming ornaments we'd bought at the ten-cent store, red and green candles, and an angel on the topmost limb.

Afterward Dux cleaned up the mess while I made cocoa and brought out cookies. Then I went to the piano and we sang all the Christmas carols, with Buddy and Lee getting off the track occasionally, and Ginger sat in her playpen watching us with solemn blue eyes.

Mother and Dad arrived on the morning of Christmas Eve, bringing Russell and Drexel. Mother and Father Gentry were to arrive later in the day. The house was shiny and clean and a coal fire in the old-fashioned grate gave out warmth and cheer. Mother and Dad were upstairs playing with Ginger, and the children were in the back yard, where Drexel was making a snow man.

It was three o'clock in the afternoon and I was in the kitchen making turkey dressing and cranberry sauce, with Dux on the job in the tasting department, when the door-bell rang. Flinging off my apron, I ran to the door and he followed me. But before we could get there the door opened and Mother and Father Gentry stood on the threshold, grinning as if they had put something over on us. And they had. We'd expected to meet them at the station, but obviously they had come on an earlier train.

" Merry Christmas! " they cried, in unison.

" Merry Christmas! " Dux and I repeated.

And Christmas had officially begun. It was a simple, homespun Christmas that we all spent together in the house in Eastover Court, with the children and the grandparents taking priority, but I have never known a happier one.

In January, Dux started to have trouble with welders. They were hard to get, and it was about this time that he stopped using couplings on pipelines in favor of welding the joints together. There was less chance of leakage, he said, in welded joints. Also, welders were needed to repair broken lines and build drips — those gadgets attached to pipelines to separate water from gas.

For a month or so he worried along, doing the best he could. Then he persuaded the head of an oxygen and acety-lene company to hold night classes to teach welding, got the men together who wanted to learn, and took the course with them.

Even to this day welders are the pace setters of pipeline construction and are still called the " prima donnas " of the trade. Dux laughed when one of my friends, who had asked him to let her see a pipeline job, remarked,

" I don't think it's fair to let *those* men have pretty umbrellas when the rest don't."

And she still didn't look convinced that he wasn't showing partiality, even when Dux explained that the shade made a difference in the efficiency of both the weld and the welder.

When Buddy started in the first grade at Emmet Field, I joined the Parent-Teacher Association, taking part in all the activities like the good, solid citizen I wanted to be. For the first six months I gloried in my son's all-A report cards and was provoked when Dux showed only a mild interest.

" Tell Buddy you're proud of him," I urged; " tell him you're glad he's going to be a good student."

Dux shook his head. " You keep telling him — that's enough." Dux believed that you spoiled children if you bragged about them, but I've never thought a pat on the back hurt anybody.

One day Buddy was late coming home from school and I was standing at the window anxiously watching for him when he came up the walk. At the sight of him, I screamed and ran to the door.

" Oh, my poor darling," I exclaimed in dismay. " Did someone hurt you? "

He wiped his bloody nose with a torn sleeve and looked up at me with one good eye. " Had a fight," he said calmly, as if it were an everyday occurrence.

" Oh, my precious, my baby! " I cried, trying to put my arms around him.

He managed to elude me and started into the house. " The other guy cried," he announced proudly.

Bewildered, I stared after him, wondering how many good mothers had fighting six-year-olds and how they coped with a situation like this, and tried to figure out just where I had erred in his training.

When Dux got home he put a piece of beefsteak on Buddy's black eye and grinned — the brute! — as if he were glad it had happened. Later, when we were alone together, I said tearfully:

" What do you suppose we should do? About Buddy, I mean? "

" Do? " Dux looked at me in astonishment. " Why, nothing, of course." He chuckled and I made a face at him. " Darling," he said, " you just don't understand boys at all, do you? I'm really proud of him now. Our Buddy is no sissy."

It didn't sound logical to me, but then men and logic didn't always mix. The next morning, after Dux left for work, I took Buddy aside and talked to him, trying to convince him that he shouldn't fight — unless, perhaps, in self-defense. But I finally decided to let Dux handle such situations. Later, when Russell came to live with us and attend school, Dux supervised boxing matches between the two boys and it stopped the fighting — at least, most of it.

That spring someone gave Dux an English setter which we named Bingo, despite the fact that she was female. We'd had puppies before, but they were " curbstone setters " that got run over before they grew up, or died of distemper, each death being a bemoaned tragedy until the pet was replaced. We had never owned a pedigreed dog before, and I decided to raise puppies.

Dux took Bingo to a veterinarian who bred her to a Lewellyn. He built her a cute little doghouse, and fenced in a long runway out near the garage. But Bingo, having a mind of her own, didn't care for the runway: she preferred the yard, since the children were there. And she didn't like her house: she preferred ours and slept on a rug at the foot of our bed. I scolded and muttered to myself as I cleaned dog hairs off the furniture, but I never could resist Bingo's liquid brown eyes, her waving tail, and her cold, quivering nose nuzzled against my hand.

When the time came for our vacation that year, we decided to leave her at a kennel. The children wanted to take her with us, but it was getting close to the time of her confinement, so that was out of the question. Besides, there really wasn't room for her in the car — what with fishing gear, camping outfits, toys, and us. All the time I was getting our things together, she kept following me around, as if she wanted to tell me something.

"You know we're going to leave you, old girl," I said, patting her head. "But never mind — we'll be back."

She licked my hand, then dropped to my feet and put her head on her paws, rolling her sad eyes at me. As if she understood, but was not quite reconciled.

While I cooked supper, Dux packed the trunk of the old Apperson Jackrabbit he'd bought secondhand. "I'll take Bingo over to Dr. Owen's tonight," he said when he'd finished. "We'll get an early start in the morning."

But when he whistled for Bingo, she didn't come. We waited awhile, then went to bed, thinking she'd gone calling for the evening, and not really worried about her. Bingo would be back, we felt sure.

The next morning we whistled and called, but still no Bingo. Dux went to look for her and I gave the children their breakfast, then told them to get into the car and wait for us. I rinsed the cereal bowls, dropped them into the pan of sudsy water, and picked up the cups, wondering all the while where Bingo could be. It wasn't like her to stay out all night; she wasn't that kind of girl.

Hearing Buddy scream, I dropped the cups and ran outside. Lee was jumping up and down beside the car, clapping her hands excitedly, and Buddy, his face beaming was running toward me.

"It's Bingo!" he shouted. "She's got babies. Mother — lots of them! Come and see."

I followed him to the car and peered inside. The back seat was a mess, the upholstery torn to shreds — but, sure enough, there was Bingo, licking the five black-and-white puppies cuddled up to her breast. There was pride in her eyes as she looked up at me — but there was something else too. "Honestly, honey," I told Dux later, when we decided to put off our vacation, "she really *did* look apologetic. And the puppies are beautiful . . ."

I know just how she feels too, I thought, and remembered that only last year I had unwittingly spoiled a vacation and we'd been obliged to compromise with a beautiful lawn!

When Dux phoned the office to say that our vacation trip was being postponed "due to reasons beyond our control," there were no embarrassing questions. Mr. Addison, in fact, seemed highly pleased.

"That's fine," he said. "There's a meeting of the Aero Club tomorrow night, and I want you to be there."

The Gas Company, he went on to explain, was about to launch a new project: aerial photography as applied to transmission and production. W. Sidney Park, an aerial photographer, was being employed to take pictures and, since the project concerned Dux's department, he was to work along with Sid Park.

This was right up Dux's alley, so to speak. Already a member of the Air Reserves and keenly interested in flying, he saw it not only as a means of enhancing his career, but as the fulfillment of a dream. A little matter like a postponed vacation was inconsequential. The fact that our Apperson Jackrabbit was somewhat the worse for having served as a stand-in for a delivery room was just one of those minor tragedies that have a way of happening even in the best of families. And the children seemed perfectly content to settle for the puppies.

Later when the Gas Company bought its own plane and Sid and Dux took their first pictures, it was thrilling to the point of goose-pimples. They photographed the area from Louisville to Madison for an electric transmission line, and it still gives me a glow of pride to realize that Dux was among the first to use aerial photography for mapping pipelines, electric transmission lines, leaseholds, and surveying.

As members of the Reserves, Sid and Dux — my husband ended up a Captain, if you please! — were among those instrumental in transforming Bowman Field from a pasture lot into a real airport. With other squadron members, they concreted the hangars and did other work on week ends. Mr. Bowman had leased the land and the U.S. Government had agreed to headquarter the Reserve Flying Squadron there, the hangars to be moved from the field at Fort Knox. Again, it was this group who dismantled, moved, and re-erected them.

Then, not to be outdone, the distaff side took a hand in the proceedings. Mrs. Addison, Margaret Park — Sid's wife — and I appointed ourselves a committee of three to see that the clubrooms were in keeping with the rest of the handsome setup. We begged secondhand tables, chests, and chairs until practically every attic in Louisville was stripped bare. We painted the furniture ourselves, in between making curtains and varnishing floors. But it was fun working together, and the results of our handiwork more than paid for tired backs, aching feet, and ragged fingernails.

Later Dux, Sid, and other pilots of the squadron flew around the country on week ends in the interest of aviation. In addition to dedicating airfields and promoting flying, they talked at luncheon clubs and helped sell local authorities on painting the names of their towns on a barn roof or flat-topped building as a convenience to flyers for identification purposes.

There were times, however, when misadventure would step in and an otherwise successful exploit would end up in red faces. There was the time when Dux and Sid flew to Harrodsburg with the rest of the squadron to dedicate the airfield, help celebrate the town's birthday, and honor George Rogers Clark, its founder. Margaret and I drove there and were entertained royally by the town's top ladies. We rode in the first car of the parade, bursting with pride in our husbands and feeling for all the world like celebrities. Then came the time for the memorial services at the grave-yard in the old Indian fort where George Rogers Clark was buried.

The local garden club ladies had gathered a tubful of daisies from the surrounding hills, and Dux and Sid were asked to strew them over the cemetery at a specified time during the ceremony. Margaret and I stood a little apart from the others, visualizing the crowd's reaction when our husbands would make this beautiful gesture on behalf of the honored dead.

It was a tense moment. The preacher had just finished his opening prayer, and the people stood at reverent attention, when the plane swooped down. Sid, apparently realizing that it would be no small feat to hit the tiny cemetery — it was only about fifty feet square, with a stone fence around it — flew quite low. In fact, he dipped so low that the crowd ducked and a few women screamed. Then he made a steep bank and Dux, harnessed in the cockpit with a gunner's belt, lifted an armful of daisies, dropping them at just the right moment. But the plane was so low the propeller blast didn't have time to scatter the flowers, and the entire bunch plopped smack-dab on top of the as-tonished preacher's head.

It wasn't funny — at least, not to us. But Captain Brown, who relayed the incident to his fellow officers in Louisville, said the entire squadron chuckled about it for days.

That summer just about ruined my disposition. Trying to be a housewife, mother, a civic do-gooder, and a social butterfly at one and the same time proved too much for me. I was so tired of diapers, dirty dishes, grocery bills that zoomed over the budget, and the feeling that we couldn't even afford Mrs. Eastlin and others to keep the children now and then!

"I don't see how we'll ever get anywhere on your salary," I told Dux. "Two dinky raises in two years — and you work so hard. Don't you ever wonder, just a little bit, if you shouldn't look for something better?"

But I got nowhere. All he would say was that he liked his job, liked the people he worked with, and that I shouldn't be so impatient.

One morning I was hurrying to get through with my work so I could meet Margaret Park downtown for lunch — we'd planned to see the new talking movie at the Strand. Mrs. Eastlin was coming at noon, and I winced at the thought of paying her a whole dollar to keep the children, but I'd reached the peak of my endurance and nothing seemed right.

I cut my finger peeling apples for the pie I was making for dinner. Then I had to stop, kiss a bump on Lee's head and rub butter on it, and finally rock her to sleep. The telephone rang twice, a wrong number each time. Thank goodness Ginger's still asleep, I thought as I got out the vacuum cleaner and went back to work.

Suddenly the vacuum cleaner stopped. I checked the electric plug, turned the cleaner upside down trying to find the trouble, but it was no use. I flung the thing from me and the handle fell on my foot. That was the last straw.

" Oh-h-h! " I wailed, dropping to the floor, " I — I just can't take any more."

" Why, baby, what's the matter? "

Surprised and a little abashed, I looked up to see Dux coming in the door. " What are you doing home at this hour? " I asked, surreptitiously drying my eyes.

" Came to get my bag," he said. " Addison and I have to go to Chicago. Now — what's the trouble? "

" The darned old vacuum's out of fix," I fumed. " Everything is, for that matter. I — I'm so tired I can't even think."

" Poor kid." He dropped down beside me, reached for the cleaner, and looked at it. Then he threw it aside, as I had done. " Never mind the cleaning — I haven't time to fix it now. Why don't you hire that little colored girl Mrs. Addison's been telling us about? "

" Ha! " I said. " We can't afford the five dollars a week, that's why! " To save my life I couldn't have kept the tears from rolling down my face. " We can't even afford the dollar we pay Mrs. Eastlin now and then."

Dux took me in his arms and we sat on the floor and talked. He told me I wasn't helping him any by wearing myself out. " No man in his right mind expects to hitch a race horse to a plow," he grinned. " We'll cut down someplace else," he said. " But I've got to know you're happy, or else none of my work is worth-while."

So we hired Winnie, an eager-to-learn young colored girl who turned out to be a jewel. We all learned to love her and to depend on her, and she could do more with the children than either Dux or I.

But I still worried about the future. I kept thinking that Dux was too good for his job, that he was overworked and underpaid, and that he was in a rut. I wanted him out of it, even if it meant leaving Louisville and the home we loved.

19

THEN, FINALLY, an opportunity came. Dux gave a talk on " the romance of natural gas " to the Kiwanis Club, and a guest from Pittsburgh came over and asked for his address. Two weeks later, Dux got a letter from him, saying he was the executive vice-president of a steel corporation in Pennsylvania and had an opening for a chief engineer. Would Dux come to Pittsburgh to discuss the position?

" Oh, honey," I cried, " a steel company! It's a wonderful chance, and I'll bet they pay wonderful salaries! "

He didn't seem nearly as impressed as I thought he should be, even said he wasn't sure he wanted to work for a steel company. " It would cost twice as much to live in Pittsburgh," he pointed out. " And we'll lose money on our house if we sell now."

" But, Dux," I argued, " you'll never get anywhere with the Gas Company — at least, not for years and years! "

" How do I know I'd get anywhere with this steel company? " He shook his head. " Besides, look who's talking. You were the one who wanted to put down roots — now what do you want to dig them up for? "

I straightened and drew a deep breath. " It's just that I think you ought to be free, Dux. Free to use your own judgment, to make decisions, oh — well, not to be hampered by red tape — "

" Every company has its red tape," he protested. " As for making decisions, using my own judgment — I do that now. What's more," he added, " Mr. Lewis and Addison depend on me."

" That's it! " I exclaimed. " You're thinking of them — not yourself and what might be happening to us." I knew how he felt about the Company, the men he worked for. A woman soon learns all those secret little things about her man, and I knew the depth of Dux's loyalty. But loyalty to others wouldn't give our children the kind of education I wanted them to have. And it wouldn't buy the kind of boat that Dux loved to talk about. " Well," I shrugged, " it's for you to say."

Dux wouldn't commit himself, though he did say he would think about it. We had a vacation coming up and, on the first day, he took a train to Pittsburgh. The steel company had written him a second letter urging him to come, expenses paid. I waited in a fever of excitement for him to come back. When the telegram finally came, telling the time of his arrival, I drove to the station to meet him.

" O.K., baby — I told them I'd take the job," he said as he kissed me. It seemed to me there was a new tone in his voice as if he were more sure of himself, more confident.

" Oh, honey, I'm so glad! " I squeezed his arm and it was all I could do to keep from skipping as we walked through the station and out to the car.

" It looks pretty good," he said. " I'll resign in a couple of weeks after I've cleared up a few things. I don't want to leave Addison in the lurch."

" How much is the salary? " I asked.

" About twice what I've been getting," he grinned.

" Oh, golly," I breathed. " We're rich! "

" Oh, yeah? " said my good and reliable balance wheel.

" Rents in Pittsburgh are practically double what they are here, food is higher, and I understand it's next to impossible to get a maid."

" Oh." My feathers fell and my dream of sudden riches took a nose dive.

" But it's definitely a step up," Dux acknowledged. " It really is an opportunity."

That made me feel better, but it wasn't until later, much later, that we found out what we'd let ourselves in for.

We found a good home for Bingo and began to pack our things. Selling the house was like parting with a beloved relative, even though we felt that no matter who lived there it would always belong to us because of the children's footprints and the signatures of friends in the garage.

We said a tearful good-by to our Louisville friends — especially the Addisons and the Parks. Mr. Addison seemed genuinely sorry to see Dux leave. " We'll miss him — but he'll go places, that boy," he said.

It was right after the stock market crash that we moved to Pittsburgh — a bad time to make any kind of move, I guess, but it didn't dim our bright hopes one iota. We weren't afraid of hardships, and I felt that for men like Dux there was always room at the top. So the future stretched out like a bright carpet before us.

We took rooms in an apartment hotel and started to look for a place to live near a good school. Pittsburgh was so different from Louisville that I was a little confused and grateful that Dux could go house-hunting with me. But on the third day we were there, before we'd found anything that measured up to our needs, Dux was sent to Tulsa on business.

" You find a place, Shortie! " he said. " Wire me where you are."

" By myself? " I asked, dismayed at the thought. " Can't we wait until you come back? "

"No; I've no idea how long I'll be gone," he said. "You've got to get the kids started in school."

At the station he put his arm around me. "Don't look so gloomy. You'll find something — my girl can do anything," he smiled.

I gave him back his smile. That old line again, I thought, remembering the engineering pants and lots of other things he cajoled me into doing; but this was different, and I wondered how I'd ever do it alone.

The next morning I started out bright and early, resolved to live up to my husband's expectations. After considerable driving around, accomplishing nothing, I found myself on Beechwood Boulevard, a lovely, homelike section of town. There, right in the middle of an attractive block, was a cute little house with a " For Rent " sign out front! The very place I've been looking for, I told myself happily.

It was near Linden School too, which I'd been told was one of the nicest in Pittsburgh. Elated, I wrote down the name on the sign, went to a telephone, and called the real-estate company. A pleasant voice informed me that someone would be out immediately to show me through the house.

As I waited for the real-estate man, I began thinking and planning what I would do with the yard. It wasn't very large — but one couldn't have everything, and it could be made to look very pretty with tulips, maybe a bit of scarlet sage, or perhaps some geraniums. The shrubs, I noted, were quite good.

" If I decide to take this," I asked the man when he came and unlocked the door, " how soon can we move in? "

" At once," he said bluntly, appraising me with curious eyes.

We walked through the hall into the living room, then

back to the dining room and into the kitchen. I caught him staring at me once or twice and, although he didn't come out and ask if I knew what I was doing, his manner inferred it.

" The kitchen is awfully small," I said, opening the cupboard doors. Uncomfortably aware of his brash appraisal I was determined to find something to pick at. Besides, I didn't want to appear too anxious. " A woman wants a lot of space when she cooks," I added in a carefully casual voice.

" This is a very choice location, madam," he said. " And I can assure you this kitchen is larger than many in the neighborhood."

I went back into the living room and stood for a moment, thinking how I'd arrange our furniture, secretly delighted with the house. What's-his-name cleared his throat and looked at his watch.

" I have another appointment," he informed me, " so, if you don't like the place — "

" I never said I didn't like it," I cut in. " And I haven't seen the upstairs yet." If he thinks he's going to rush me, I thought, he's crazy. After all, I'm his customer.

He took it a little easier after that, though his eyes continued to register a kind of resigned boredom that made me angry. We went upstairs, even into the attic, then down to the basement and out to the garage. " I'll take it," I said finally, " but I won't sign a lease for more than a year."

" Madam," he said haughtily, " aren't you even interested in the price? "

I favored him with as scornful a smile as I could contrive at the moment. After all, I reasoned, this was only a little old three-bedroom house, not even as big as the one we'd sold back in Louisville. It couldn't possibly rent for more than eighty dollars a month — and with Dux's new salary

I certainly wasn't going to pinch pennies in the matter of rent. Anyway, I didn't like this man's attitude.

" Oh, the rental won't bother me," I announced airily.

" Well — " he paused to stare at me, " it's bothered most of the prospective tenants. That's why it's vacant. Not many people want to pay three hundred a month — "

" Three hundred a month! " I gasped. " For *this*? "

He nodded, smiling for the first time. " You're new in Pittsburgh, aren't you? "

A flush started creeping up my neck, into my face. " Y-yes," I gulped. " I — I never dreamed . . . Thanks for your trouble." I turned and ran out to my car.

" Good luck," he called after me. I didn't need to look back to know that he was laughing to himself.

With a vicious gesture, I turned on the ignition and put the car into motion, fuming inwardly.

After six unfruitful days of house-hunting, I decided to leave the furniture in storage at Louisville and settled for a furnished apartment. It consisted of a moderate-size living room with rollaway beds in a closet, two tiny bedrooms, a bathroom that you almost had to back into, and a kitchenette no bigger than our hall closet back home. Even so, the rental took a sizable chunk out of our income, and we never did get used to the lack of space.

Determined to send the children to the Linden School, I had to wangle a special permit from the superintendent of education, as it was out of our district. The going and coming involved so many bus changes that it was necessary for me to drive them to and from school, and they took their lunches along with them. The only alternative was traveling by taxicab.

The children were good sports, but I could see they missed their friends, though it didn't take them long to get acquainted. Most of all they missed Russell, who had gone back to West Liberty.

Dux was away for over two weeks on that first trip, and I hoped it would be the last one — for a while, at least. But his first words, as we drove home from the depot, were, " Golly, it's good to be home "; his second, " I've got to be in Clovis, New Mexico, in ten days."

And that was the way it went. The Pittsburgh story, in so far as Dux was concerned, might well be described as a running record entitled " Here Today; Gone Tomorrow."

He was home, of course, for Christmas, but in the early part of January he left again, this time for Fort Worth, Texas. He was figuring reserves in the gas and oil areas, supervising the building of compressor stations and pipelines. Money was tight, and most of the pipe and supplies were being sold for whatever cash could be obtained and the balance taken in mortgage bonds. Dux did all the appraisal work to make certain the bonds would pay out.

But, as a family, we weren't happy. The money didn't mean as much as I'd thought it would. Even getting out of debt and having a substantial savings account didn't make up for our unsettled way of life. Either I was going places with Dux, worrying about the children, or I was staying home with them, worrying about Dux.

So fall passed, winter came, and suddenly it was spring. The Depression, heretofore regarded as a temporary setback that would soon blow over, became a painful reality. The company cut all salaries in half and, financially, we were right back where we started — plus heavier expenses and higher rent. True, Dux was at home nights, working days in the office, but we did not feel the same sense of security that we had felt with the Gas Company. As Dux pointed out, utilities seldom pay as much as individual companies, but they almost never cut salaries and usually stand by their employees in times of distress.

We were also plagued by a vague sense of aloneness, prompting me to say, " Yes — and it's one thing to be up against it among strangers; something else again, among friends."

We were feeling pretty low when, like a bolt out of the blue, the steel company ordered Dux to Kentucky to bid on an oil line which was to run from Horse Cave to Louisville. Instantly we were in a fever of excitement. If the bid was accepted, that would mean Dux would build the line and we could return to Louisville. It seemed almost too good to be true!

But it did come true. It was on a Saturday and the children and I were eating lunch when Dux phoned to report the glad news. " Get packed, Shortie," he told me, and there was a lilt to his voice. " I've got the job sewed up. Notify the landlord you're giving up the apartment right away. I won't be able to get back there. You come on as soon as you can."

" We're practically in Louisville right now! "

Choking back a sob of happiness, I ran to tell the children. " Look," I said, " I'll scoot out and see the landlord, then start packing. You finish your dessert and wash up the dishes."

Poor kids, I thought, they're always having to look after themselves. I hurried out to see the apartment manager about our unexpired lease, and was agreeably surprised to find that it didn't matter about the lease. " I've a long waiting list," he told me. " Plenty of people will be glad to snap up such a desirable apartment."

" They're welcome to it," I said, without malice, " I'm going *home!* "

It was after midnight before I got to bed that night. But everything was packed, the apartment cleaned, and our clothes ready to hop into the moment we woke up. I set the alarm clock for four A.M., thinking that if we got an early start, we might drive the distance from Pittsburgh to Louisville in one day.

It was still dark when our car, loaded to the gills, including Tippy, a barking mongrel that somehow we'd become attached to, started out of the apartment house driveway. A shrill whistle stopped me and I looked around to see a burly policeman peering into the car. Tippy growled at him.

" You belong in there, lady? " He jerked a thick thumb toward the apartment building we'd just left.

" We did," I answered, wondering what business it was of his. " But we're leaving."

" Going back to Loo-ville," Lee chanted.

Ginger picked up the refrain and began in a singsong voice, " Goin' back to Loo-ville. Goin' back — "

Tippy barked his approval and Buddy tried to quiet him. Suddenly the officer's flashlight was turned full into my face and I threw my hand up against the glare.

" Take that thing out of my eyes," I snapped. " And get your foot off the running board. We're in a hurry."

" Yeah. That's what I'm thinking," he said gruffly. " Too danged much of a hurry, if you ask me."

" Nobody's asking you," I said hotly, determined to hold my ground.

" You wait right here, sister."

He turned and walked into the apartment house. Absently, I explained to Ginger that no, he really didn't think I was his sister, and seethed inwardly at his impudence and the delay he was causing. I started to drive on, but noticed his motorcyle leaning against a lamppost. I knew he'd catch me, so I turned off the motor.

After what seemed like hours, but must have been only a few minutes, he came back. " It's all right, lady," he said sheepishly. " I got the manager up and talked to him."

" And will you please tell me what difference that makes? " I flared, stepping on the starter and wishing I could bang him on the head.

" Thought you were tryin' to beat your rent," he said. " Been a lot of that lately. You can move on now."

" Of all things! " I muttered. Pulling the gear into first, I shot past him, knowing that I was in a fifteen-mile zone, and practically daring him to follow me. With a motor-cycle at his disposal, the remarkable thing was that he *didn't!*

20

Iт didn't take us long to get settled in Louisville. We rented a house, got our furniture out of storage, and soon it was as if we'd never gone away. Dux's salary cut didn't matter so much here, and even the lowering clouds of the Depression were not too disconcerting. We had experienced stormy weather before and survived. Besides, we had health, a strong sense of optimism born of faith in the rightness of things, and we were surrounded by friends. Nothing could touch us — or so I chose to believe.

By the time Dux had completed the pipeline from Horse Cave into a Louisville refinery, however, the whole country was in the grip of the Depression. A letter from his employers informed Dux that they didn't think it worth the gamble of traveling expense in order to try to get business for the time being. He was to sit tight, hold his horses, so to speak, and wait the thing out. Meanwhile, all expense accounts were being canceled.

Dux was never one to sit things out. And so, as time passed, he grew increasingly restless, even despondent — and, yes, hard to live with. Not that he meant to be disagreeable — oh, no! He was just preoccupied, moody, bitterly resentful of the enforced idleness.

He would lie awake nights, hour after hour, as if by doing so he could find some solution to a problem that the entire country was beginning to regard as insoluble. I too would lie awake, staring silently into the darkness, racking my brain for ways and means to pull this stranger who was my husband out of this seemingly bottomless quagmire that threatened to engulf all of us.

When the children got into his hair — which was often — I was the helpless bystander that got hurt. I knew Dux didn't mean it that way. He was a devoted father, an adoring husband. His real concern was for us — what would happen to us if things grew worse instead of better. It didn't occur to him that, in his anxiety, he might be defeating his own purpose. We wanted the old Dux back — the gay, laughing Dux. Never mind the Depression.

The situation became keenly acute one hot afternoon in June when even the weather seemed to have gone in cahoots with the general unrest. I was fixing dinner and the children were playing in the back yard, their young voices coming through the open kitchen window. I stopped shredding cabbage to listen. Buddy said, " Shush, kids, here comes Dad." The sudden silence that followed spoke volumes and, involuntarily, I winced. Then I heard Dux's voice — that strange, new voice with an edge to it — saying:

" How many times have I told you children to keep your junk off the driveway? Howard, get that dern bike out of my way! " He never called Buddy " Howard " unless he was cross.

Wearily, I turned back to my work. How much longer would this black mood last? Dux ought to know it did no earthly good to worry himself sick. It would only make bad matters worse and certainly wouldn't stop the Depression.

He came in, tired-looking and pale, and kissed me hello. I gave him a cup of coffee. " Here — drink this. Why don't you lie down till dinner is ready? "

" No, I feel fine." He sank onto the kitchen stool, shoulders sagging, a picture of defeat.

" I wish you wouldn't take things so hard. Business is bound to get better. Someday I'll bet you'll look back and laugh at yourself for worrying."

" You just don't understand business, dear." He smiled glumly and his dark-ringed eyes wandered over the room. " I hate to see you working in this hot kitchen."

" I like to cook. I'm good too." I held up the dish of fluffy graham-cracker pie for him to see, but he sat staring out the window, a faraway look in his eyes.

Buddy burst into the room, the screen door banging behind him. Dux jumped. " For gosh sake," he shouted, " must you always slam doors? "

" Sorry, Dad," Buddy said cheerfully. Lifting the lid of the soup kettle, he sniffed, rolling his eyes upward. " When do we eat, Mother? I'm starved."

" You always are, Son." I pushed his grimy hand away and turned to Dux. " Honey, when you were thirteen, were you just an appetite with skin around it? " I laughed, trying to make conversation.

" I hope I had better manners. And look at you, young man," Dux said. " How in thunder do you manage to ruin your clothes? "

" Baseball." Buddy tucked in the tail of his torn shirt and said excitedly, " Dad, we had three men on base when — "

" Never mind," Dux broke in. " Go call your sisters and wash your hands for dinner."

Buddy turned and the back door banged. " If you do that again," Dux called, " I'll tan your hide."

I caught the door as the three children came in and raced to the bathroom. Dux got up to help me carry the food to the table and, as he started through the swinging door to the dining room, Lee bounded in from the other side. Soup splashed on the floor and an angry flush spread over Dux's face. Lee's blue eyes filled with tears.

" For heaven's sake," I exclaimed, " get to the table, all of you. I'll wipe it up."

We ate our soup in silence. I carried the bowls to the kitchen and dumped them in the sink, brought in the peas and potatoes, and started back for the meat when a whistle sounded outside. Buddy looked at me apprehensively.

" The boys are going to the carnival tonight, Dux," I said casually. " It's the last night."

Dux's face froze. " For Pete's sake, do kids nowadays have to be going places every minute? He went to the movies last night." He looked at me suspiciously. " Where does he get money for carnivals? "

" He earned it," I answered proudly, " cutting grass in the neighborhood."

" Anyhow, Dad, scouts get in for half price," Buddy chimed in, and squirmed as the whistle came again.

" Well, I think you'd better start finding your fun at home for a change." Dux threw down his napkin and got up. " Go tell those boys you can't go."

I couldn't meet Buddy's stricken eyes. Long ago my husband and I had agreed not to interfere in the matter of discipline. I looked down at the white knuckles of my hand, still gripping the pot holder. " It's vacation time, Dux, honey," I ventured.

" I don't give a darn if it is. You'd spoil these kids rotten if I'd let you."

As he strode from the room, I looked after the man I'd promised to love and thought of the plan I'd been mulling over in my mind, trying to make up my mind what I should do.

Buddy went outside. " What's the matter with Daddy, Mommy? " Ginger asked.

" He's sick, darling," I answered absently, wondering if I could make Dux realize what he was doing to us.

Sniffing the air, I cried, " My chops! " ran to the kitchen, and jerked open the oven door. A billow of black smoke brought tears to my eyes. I slammed the door shut and turned off the gas, my mind made up. " I won't put up with living like this another single day," I muttered to myself. " I'll do it tonight. When he starts walking the floor, as he's done for weeks, I'll have *my* say! "

About three o'clock I wakened to see Dux sitting in the moonlight, his face buried in his hands. I fought down the sudden surge of pity and said:

" Might as well turn on the light. I'm awake too."

" Sorry, honey. I just can't seem to sleep."

I drew a deep breath and said: " No, of course you can't. You can't do anything but feel sorry for yourself. You're all wrapped up in your nice little hell. Too bad you've got us on your hands! "

He turned on the light and regarded me with hurt, puzzled eyes. " But it's only for you and the children that I — "

" Oh, don't give me that," I interrupted, avoiding his eyes and forcing myself to continue. " You aren't thinking of us. If you were, you'd snap out of this and stop making us miserable. I thought I'd married a man, not a — er — a weakling who's afraid of a little adversity."

Dux grabbed his clothes and started jerking them on. " That's hitting below the belt. You don't understand — "

" Oh, piffle. Stop telling me that! I may be dumb about some things, but I've got brains enough to see where you're heading." I had to say it, though I was sure it was hurting me as much as Dux. " When business *does* come back, you won't get anywhere. You'll be a wreck. And where will we be then? The children and I haven't any security except our faith in you — and you're letting us down."

He jerked open the bedroom door. " I can't take any more of this! I never thought *you'd* turn against me! " He left the room, hurried down the stairs, and an instant later, I heard the front door slam.

I buried my face in the pillow. Dux would never forgive me; much as I loved my family, I wished I were a thousand miles away. How could I ever have thought such foolish strategy would help? Miss Abby would throw up her hands in horror if she could know about this, I thought.

Presently I put on a robe and started downstairs. Buddy's door opened a crack and he whispered,

" Did it work? " Evidently he had overheard us. I had told him about my plan the night before. My face burned with shame.

" I'm afraid not, Son. Come on down and I'll make us some lemonade." I felt that I had to do something, if only to steady my reeling brain.

I squeezed lemons, and Buddy got the glasses, his young face showing concern. " Dad got mad, didn't he? I heard the front door slam."

I nodded. " I guess he's gone for a walk. I — I tried to tell him off, but it didn't work out the way I hoped it would. I've made a mess of things."

Buddy gathered up the lemon rinds and put them in the garbage can. " Are we awful poor, Mother? " he asked.

" It depends on how you look at things, honey," I said thoughtfully. " We haven't much money, of course, but most people don't have nowadays. But we've got things money can't buy — like love for one another, our health, having fun and being together. Those are the important things." At least, we *did* have them, I qualified mentally.

But now I've spoiled everything. What if Dux shouldn't come back!

Buddy drank his lemonade and I sipped at mine. I sensed his anxiety and hated having him see me so upset. We looked at each other as the front door opened softly, and sat very still. Then the kitchen door swung open and Dux stood on the threshold, a sheepish grin on his face.

I jumped up and threw myself into his arms. " Oh, Dux, I'm sorry. I didn't mean any of those hateful things I said. I was wrong, darling, terribly wrong."

He hugged me close, as if he'd never let me go. " No, I was wrong, Shortie. Guess I was so woolgathered I couldn't see the honey for the bees." He released me to smile at Buddy, who was watching the little scene with unconcealed relief. " Better get back to bed, Sonny. Your mother and I have things to talk about. As of now, this very moment, we're taking a holiday from worry."

If business was taking a holiday, we decided — well, so would we. We would spend the rest of the summer having fun, grateful that Dux was home and we could all be together. There would be no more walking of floors, no more sleepless nights, no more self-imposed headaches over conditions we could not control.

Instead, we would learn how to play again, get back to the fundamentals, the simple things of life, enjoy the blessings that were ours for the taking. And that is precisely what we did.

Russell came down to spend the summer and Dux's young nephew, from New Jersey, came for a visit. True, we had to watch our pennies, but we had fun — going on picnics, driving out to the boat club, where Dux's membership was already paid. Or going out to Big Springs Golf Club, also prepaid, for a game of golf or just to sit with friends on the broad veranda. With Dux as tutor and the three boys taking turns as caddies, I learned to play such a good game of golf that one spectator remarked, " It's hard to tell the pupil from the teacher." It might have gone to my head too, if I hadn't chosen that very moment to miss a short putt!

It was a summer to remember. Even today we recall it with a sense of nostalgia, grateful for what it gave us. The children, now with families of their own, often refer to it as " that time when we didn't have any money — and had so much fun! " Although it cost us virtually nothing, it paid off in health, happiness, and a finer sense of values for us all. And when business did come back, Dux was ready for it.

21

Dux read the trade magazines religiously, and said often that he was sure he could get enough business to pay his salary, at least. But when he wrote the steel company to that effect, he got the same old run-around answer: business was practically at a standstill; nothing to do but hope — and wait.

As I must have said before, Dux isn't a good waiter. Finally he made up his mind to take a sales trip at his own expense. "They can't shoot me for trying," he said as I packed his bag, wondering what we'd use for money if the trip proved a blooper. "I'll call on the utilities and oil companies. With most of the salesmen off the road, surely I can scrape up something. If not, I'll come right home."

His first letter told of enough orders for pipe and fittings to warrant sending in an expense account to his company. That must have surprised the pessimists!

Dux's next letter said he was going on to Michigan, to look into a newly discovered gas formation there. "I've got an idea in the back of my head," he wrote. "If it works, we'll move to Michigan. I'll phone you when I know."

I began, immediately, to pack. By this time packing had become a habit with me. To say I could do it with my eyes shut is only a mild exaggeration. And I could move at the crack of a whip, so to speak.

At the end of the second week Dux phoned to say he'd made a deal to do consulting work for a utility company. There was a good chance for a pipeline too. The children and I were to come as soon as we could.

" But do be careful driving," he warned. I'd heard that before too — and will probably hear it till the last day I live!

So, once again, we stored the furniture, crowded into the car with our personal belongings — minus our poor little dog, Tippy, who'd recently met death at the hands of a speed demon — and headed for Michigan. There was no police interference this time, no apartment lease to worry about, and even leaving our beloved Louisville wasn't too great an emotional strain. We were going to Dux. Life wasn't any fun without him.

Our destination was Jackson, Michigan, an up-and-coming little city in the south-central part of the state. We arrived there tired and hungry, but too excited over this new adventure to mind. Dux had pleasant rooms for us at the Hayes Hotel and it was wonderful being together again. Dux's work took him all over the state, and for a week the children and I went with him, enthralled by the beauty of Michigan, the stately trees, the broad highways, the countless lakes.

" Do you know," Dux said, " if a man wanted to fish in a different lake every day, it would take him eleven and a half years? "

" You sound like a chamber of commerce talking," I teased, though I had to admit I shared his enthusiasm and was thrilled when he said, dreamily:

" Someday we'll own a bit of this water wonderland. In the meantime you pick the town where you want to live and let's get settled; it's almost time for school."

We chose Jackson — why, I don't know. Maybe because of its location in relation to Dux's work. Maybe because of its homelike atmosphere and its magnificent cascades, or its friendly people — or, well, just because. We loved it then, and we love it now. There is an old saying that you can take the gal out of Kentucky, but you can't get Kentucky out of the gal. And yet, here I was, turning traitor to my native state!

We rented a furnished house, took a year's lease, and enrolled the children in school. Buddy entered the freshman class at high school; Lee began her first year at intermediate; and Ginger, fifth-grade grammar. Mother, Dad, and Russell came for a visit, and Russell stayed to enter the freshman class with Bud. Almost before we realized it we had begun to put down roots.

About that time Dux and I began to get ideas — crazy ideas, our friends said, because the country was still in the throes of the Depression. Dux saw unlimited possibilities in the new oil and gas fields, and we began to visualize a business of our own. This had been our goal from the start. For six solid months we mulled the thing over in our minds.

"You couldn't pick a worse time," our friends said. "There's a Depression on — or didn't you know?"

We certainly did know there was a Depression on. Hadn't we felt the pinch of it straight through from the start? But what were we supposed to do — fold up and quit?

Finally Dux took time by the forelock, resigned from the steel company, and incorporated his own company. He chose the name and I chose the colors that were to be our insignia — Tacoma cream and Washington blue. At last, I thought, we're on our way!

Financing the operation was by no means a simple proposition, what with the Depression in full sway and practically everyone talking poormouth. It required considerable doing on Dux's part, his every ounce of ingenuity and resourcefulness, not to mention endless work. In that perilous era life was no gravy train for anyone, and the Gentrys were not exceptions.

Through the years we had managed to accumulate a small savings account — so small, in fact, that judged by today's standards it would seem infinitesimal. Dux insisted I take that and make a down payment on a home, since we hadn't had one in five years — and I guess there's nothing like a home to give one a sense of stability and assurance. In our case we felt that a home was essential, not only to ourselves but to the well-being of our children, who were rapidly growing up.

" I'll take my last expense check," Dux said, " and earn what I can from consulting fees."

" Hadn't you better take the savings account? " I asked, knowing that his final expense check from the steel company amounted to less than a thousand dollars. It seemed all too little to go into business on.

But Dux, his eyes fastened on the stars and his feet set firmly on the ground, didn't think so. We would make out, he said. At least, we couldn't be hung for trying. " If I can't bring in a decent return by the time the money runs out, then I'll get a job."

Dux didn't have to go back to a job. In due time, he made connections with two oil and gas companies to be their engineering consultant on a retaining fee basis. The aggregate assured us of an income at least as good as the one we'd had from the steel company.

Then, not content to stand still, Depression or no, he took up supervisory work on the drilling of gas wells. When the wells were completed, he obtained contracts to connect them, by means of short lines, or gathering lines, into the main pipelines. He was growing, branching out — and so was the business.

He obtained contracts to build meter stations, designed and built wellhead heaters and drips. Later, he managed to buy a small drilling rig and started pressure drilling. Thanks to his long hours of study, he was able to design and build most of the equipment and his method eliminated fires and blowouts and saved considerable natural gas. Because of his previous experience in putting out oil- and gas-well fires, many fields called for his services on a freelance basis and he became known as a professional fire fighter. All these things began to bring in rewards that kept our company alive.

Thus, in time, Dux was able to accumulate enough machinery and good will to serve as a nucleus for a larger and more comprehensive business that was to come later. He was also accumulating men — and acquiring a payroll that was sometimes hard to meet. And thereby hangs the tale of a gas fire that I regarded then — and still do — as a miracle in disguise.

We had been in business for something like eight months and were coming home late from a party one night when Dux's preoccupation prompted me to say:

" What's wrong, honey? You've been quiet all evening. Your mind seems so far away."

He braked the car in our driveway and drew a long breath. " Payroll's due next week and I haven't enough to meet it," he said. " I don't know what to do."

" But I thought the pipeline you've been working on was just about finished — " I began, unwilling to believe that the situation was as serious as Dux's manner inferred.

" It will be next week. But it'll take another week or ten days to get the last estimate and we're not well enough established to borrow from the bank against it."

I was silent, wondering how long a business could run without meeting its payroll. Not long, I felt sure. Besides, we couldn't do without our salary any more than our men could. But I brushed the worry aside, confident that Dux would think of a way out of this dilemma; he always did.

" I'm not sleepy. How about some waffles? " I said as I got out of the car.

" Good," Dux said. " I'm sure I can't sleep either."

While he put the car away, I went into the kitchen, kicked off my high-heeled slippers, tied an apron over my evening dress, and got out the waffle iron. Dux came in, wandered restlessly around, then perched himself on the high kitchen stool and absently watched me measure coffee and mix batter.

" You know," he said presently, " we really *are* in a jam this time."

" But something — "

" Now don't tell me something will turn up," he interrupted. " It's all very well to be optimistic, but this time it's serious."

" You've still go four days," I persisted, pouring the batter onto the hot griddle. " A lot can happen in four days."

" It'll take more than just a lot this time," he said. " *This* time, it'll take a miracle."

I set the maple sirup on the kitchen table, placed a knife beside the butter, and poured the steaming coffee.

" Forget it, honey — at least, until you eat this," I said and forked a golden brown waffle onto his plate.

" It's not that easy — forgetting it," he said gloomily. " Everyone told us we were crazy to start our own business in the middle of a Depression. Could be, they were right."

" No, they weren't," I said, and hoped my voice sounded convincing. " Wait and see. You've worked too hard to lose everything now — something will turn up."

I poured more batter onto the griddle and we ate in silence. There didn't seem to be anything I could say or do to cheer Dux up. Then suddenly he chuckled and I looked up questioningly.

" My mother used to say, ' In time of trouble, count your blessings.' Now I know what we'll do if we fail," he said. " We'll open a ' Ye Waffle Shoppe ' and you'll serve the customers in shimmering satin with a gardenia in your hair." He laughed as if he'd said something terribly funny.

Looking at him fondly, I thought, It's the formula of our entire life together — nine parts laughter, and one part tears. Just then the telephone rang.

" Who the heck could that be at this hour? " Dux groaned as he went to answer it.

" Your miracle," I called after him, hopefully.

And sure enough it was! A gas well on fire. It meant cash in the bank as soon as the fire was put out.

In less than twenty minutes we were on the highway, Dux's asbestos suits and other fire-fighting paraphernalia in the back of the car. By this time the children were old enough to look after themselves, so I left a note on the kitchen table for my cook-by-the-day, and went along. I couldn't bear the idea of staying behind, wondering and worrying. Besides, this was one fire I wanted to be in on. It was the miracle, the blessing in disguise, that saved our payroll.

22

THE OLD SAYING, "What's one man's loss is another's gain," might easily have been invented for a business such as ours, although, boiled down, it was really a matter of service that kept it alive and growing. Dux soon became known in the oil and gas fields as a " trouble shooter " — an elastic term which included the capping of wild wells, handling craters, putting out well fires, and practically anything in which the average operator was not experienced.

Oil-well fires are spectacular things, especially when seen at night. Silhouetted against the darkness, they seem like live monsters rising out of the ground, belching flame and sending up billows of black smoke, bent on destroying everything within reach.

One of the most dramatic fires that Dux was hired to put out happened in one of the larger oil fields in the northern part of Michigan. When the call came, Dux flew his plane to the well and I followed with his asbestos outfits and other fire equipment that was always carried in the back of his car. Miles before I got to the well, I could smell the smoke and see its huge billowy blackness curling into the sky and now and then a tip of the red blaze. As I drew nearer I could smell the scorched trees and the hot metal.

Traffic on the roads around the field presented a real problem — everybody in the state, it seemed, wanted to see the fire.

A policeman on guard refused to let me in till I showed him my driver's license. He pointed to the crowd of people just outside the field and said, apologetically:

" My orders are to keep everyone out who doesn't belong in there. You'd be surprised, but folks tell all kinds of tales trying to get in."

I nodded. " Yes — I can imagine. Sight-seers don't realize how they hamper the fire fighters."

" No, ma'am," he said, " they don't. They don't even seem to worry about some of those gobs of oil that fly out and hit the ground still burning."

One of our men who had been waiting showed me where to park and took some things from the car. " Mr. Gentry said for you to wait here," he shouted above the noise.

I got out of the car to watch and felt the ground shake under my feet. I could feel heat and see the rolling, roaring flames shoot high into the air, then mushroom out into a huge umbrella of red heat and smoke, searing and melting the helpless spider-web framework of the derrick, then recede as if to gather strength for the next sudden spurt upward. Often they would drop globules of oil that did not burn until they were almost to the ground.

As I watched, I saw the nearby treetops catch fire and men rush the hose nearer, turning the nozzle upward so that the fire-killing water sprayed over them in a steady stream. Men behind shields began cutting down the trees and the bulldozers with winches dragged them away.

Other men were busy dragging what was left of the twisted metal derrick and other hot debris away from the wellhead, where it could cool. This is one of the biggest parts of the whole job, Dux says, for if every bit of debris isn't pulled away, the least spark will reignite the raining oil. For this purpose they use hooks made on steel bars and tempered as hard as is possible, the debris being pulled away with wire lines fastened to these hooks.

Men on bulldozers pushed up a dirt dike around the well. For their protection, large shields of corrugated metal had been placed in front of the fire, and these were being sprayed with continuous streams of water. Dux had explained to me the reason for these dikes. They were to catch the oil after the fire was put out, so that it could be piped into a temporary sump and then pumped into storage tanks or pipelines.

A reporter from a Detroit newspaper came over. " Isn't this something? " he shouted above the noise of the fire. " We saw the flame miles away. There must be hundreds of people out there." He waved an arm to indicate the crowd. " Fit to be tied because the cops won't let 'em in."

Dux came and sat with us while he drank a cup of coffee from the Thermos. His clothes were grimy and his face streaked with soot. " Go into town, Shortie," he told me, taking the cotton out of his ears for a moment. " Get some sandwiches and coffee. And cigarettes. No telling how long we'll be here."

By the time I got back it was nearly dark, but the glare of the fire made it as light as day around the field. Cars still lined the roads, and there were policemen at every entrance. The reporter and press photographer were still hanging around.

Dux took short cat naps on the back seat of the car whenever he could, for he knew it might be days before he could get to bed. At midnight I went back into town, got the disgruntled restaurant owner out of bed and helped him make coffee and sandwiches.

At the gate I handed the policeman a chocolate bar,

drove back to the parking place, and gave the sandwiches to Dux and several other bone-weary men sprawled on the ground. Black as minstrel men, they were, and I thought, Even their own mothers wouldn't recognize them.

By noon the next day everything that would burn had been cleared away from the well. Dux sat in the car for a few minutes while he smoked a cigarette and drank a glass of milk. Then he went back to the fire, pulling down the hood of his asbestos suit and tightening the drawstring.

I have never made any pretense of bravery: I'm just an ordinary woman with ordinary capacities, taking each day as it comes and doing the best I know how. As I watched Dux going into that fiery furnace, I prayed as I'd never prayed before, and that moment seemed an eternity that passed in timeless seconds.

The fire chuckled and snorted, sending its vicious tentacles upward, while the curtain of water fell between the fire fighters and the flames. Breathing must be terrible, I thought. That intense heat must cut their lungs like knife blades!

Most oil-well fires are put out by explosives, but in this case they weren't permitted. There were too many farm houses nearby, and high explosives would break windows, mirrors, or perhaps cause worse damage.

There were other wells being drilled in the area and, since fire always takes priority, Dux and the owner of the burning well were able to borrow a number of steam boilers. These were connected together so that their steam flowed into an eight-inch pipeline, laid as close as possible to the well head. Three four-inch " snuff " lines were rigged so they could be raised or lowered as needed. Water and mud were continually pumped around the well and inside the dike.

Although I had to spend a lot of time running errands,

I was there when they turned on the eight-inch steam valve. The steam rushed out of the snuff lines, and a million tiny particles of hot mist surged into the base of the flame. For a breathless moment it looked as if the blaze had been conquered. Then, suddenly, the fire broke through the vapor and, with a violent roar, blazed up again. The steam was turned off while the height and angle of the snuff lines were readjusted, then turned on again.

Holding my breath, I watched the steam stab into the flames once more. This time, the fire receded lower and lower until finally it went out. Dux's job was finished and the oil company took over.

For a second there was dead silence. Then the spectators began to shout and honk their automobile horns. Such a round of applause would have satisfied any professional actor. The whole thing did have the aspects of a theatrical performance — and it had lasted fifty-two hours!

It was a weary, soot-begrimed Dux who staggered out to the car where I was waiting. Without a word he climbed into the back seat and stretched out. I was glad I'd had the presence of mind to bring a pillow along. The Detroit newspaper reporter came toward us, his notebook open, pencil in hand.

" Mr. Gentry," he began, " how does it feel to — "

But Mr. Gentry was dead to the world for the time being. Except for an occasional cat nap, he hadn't closed his eyes for two days and nights!

23

Dux has laid many river crossings and hundreds of miles of pipelines since that long-ago day when he went against orders to obtain experience that Mr. Addison said he didn't have. Many changes have taken place. Methods as outmoded as the old-fashioned wash kettle have been replaced with modern equipment. But new methods bring new problems to take the place of old, and the Saint Clair River crossing proved to be the most enigmatic of them all. This project was part of a hundred-and-twenty-five-mile pipeline that would carry petroleum products from Ohio to Sun Oil Company, Ltd., refinery in Canada.

"Most of the contractors will bid the job on the basis of laying the line off barges," Dux said. "I've got to figure a way to do it cheaper — if I'm going to get it." And so with pencil and paper, a pack of cigarettes, and a pot of coffee, he worked far into the night. But when he came upstairs I could tell by his face that he was satisfied.

"Got it figured?" I said, putting my magazine down and stifling a yawn. I've never been able to go to sleep until Dux comes to bed, even though I'm usually up long before he is in the morning.

"Yeah," he said, dropping one shoe to the floor and holding the other in mid-air. "I've got two problems — the current running at the rate of three miles per hour, and a

boat going or coming on an average of every twelve minutes in each twenty-four hours, so that the channel can't
be blocked. But I think I've got it licked."

" Can't you do it piecemeal — half at a time? "

" No. The channel is barely wide enough for two boats
to pass. But I'm going to put that pipeline right under
those boats while they're running — that is, if I get the
job." He dropped the other shoe and for a moment stared
off into space.

" It's got to be far enough under the river bottom to
comply with the new Saint Lawrence waterway depths;
it's got to have heavy protective coating to give it nega-
tive buoyancy and prevent corrosion," he said as if he were
memorizing a lesson. " It's got to be laid at a uniform grade
to reduce the strain on the pipe."

" Ye gods! " I exclaimed. " Anything else? "

He grinned. " Yeah — it should be done in one day!
That is, after everything's ready "; then added, " But I
haven't got it, yet." He turned out the light and kissed me
good night.

He did get the job. Immediately he went into action,
renting a suction dredge and derrick scow and starting
men digging the ditch. " I told them to make it five feet
deeper than the ' specs ' call for," he said to me. " That'll
make a twelve-foot trench." We were standing on the
riverbank at the time and I started to ask him why it had
to be so deep, but just then one of his men called to him, so
I had to use my own imagination.

We took a room in a pleasant little wayside inn near the
job while the work was in progress, and I wasn't the only
bystander to watch the goings on. Cars lined the highway,
and many of the " sidewalk superintendents " stayed for
hours, some taking movies and still pictures of each phase
of the job.

Nearly three thousand feet of heavy pipe were unloaded in the field and a swath of almost a thousand feet cut back through the trees in a wooded area on the American side. Forty-foot joints were welded together in sections six hundred feet long and placed side by side. The ends of each section were sealed. I thought the purpose of this might be to keep the rabbits out, but Dux said it was done so that the pipe could be pumped full of water for the pressure test.

I watched for a while one morning, then went back to the inn to write letters. I hadn't been gone more than five minutes when a joint of pipe, unequal to the high test, exploded, showering splinters of steel over Dux and Pete Hunter, one of his workmen. They were rushed into town to a doctor. I didn't know about it until another workman brought Dux into our room at the inn and I saw the bandage over his eye.

" Oh, Dux! " I cried. " W-what — "

" I'm all right, Shortie," he broke in. "Just got a sliver of steel in my eye when the bull-plug blew out." He sank down into a chair. I jerked a pillow from the bed, placed it behind his head, and pushed a chair up for his feet.

"Doctor says he's got to be kept quiet," the workman was saying. " Said he could lose the sight of that eye."

" Oh, no! " I quavered. " Help me get him into bed."

" I'm all right," Dux repeated weakly, and motioned to the man. " You get back to the job and let me know to-night if the rest of the sections test O.K."

" But you got to take it easy, Mr. Gentry." The workman looked sternly at Dux. " It was *three* slivers they took out of that eye," he whispered to me as he started out the door.

I took Dux's pajamas and robe from the closet and began to unlace his shoes. " You're going to get right into bed," I told him.

He let me help him undress and I knew he felt much worse than he'd admit. It hurt me to look at him; he was so white, so still, and even his good eye was bloodshot. I read to him until he fell asleep. Then I sat watching him, gripping the arms of the chair to keep from crying.

What if Dux should lose his eyesight, I kept asking myself over and over again. It would be the end of everything for him. Sickeningly conscious of my helplessness, I could only pray that this dreadful thing would not happen. It was one nightmare that I couldn't face.

The next afternoon we drove into town to have the bandage changed. " How's Pete? " Dux asked while the doctor was working on him.

" He's all right," the doctor said. " Took a couple hundred pieces of steel out of his arms, but the cuts weren't deep. You two were sure lucky."

" Then his sight will be all right? " I broke in.

There was a moment's hesitation and I held my breath for the doctor's answer. " It's a little too soon to tell," he said. " But I'd say there's some improvement. Keep him as quiet as possible and come back at this time tomorrow."

On the fourth day the doctor pronounced Dux out of danger of losing his eyesight, but said he should take it easy for a while longer.

He doesn't know Dux, I thought, and how impossible it would be to make him " take it easy." But I promised to try and breathed a sigh of relief, grateful that my prayers had been answered.

Just as I'd expected, when we came to the job on our way back to the inn — that's as far as we got. All my arguing didn't convince Dux that he should go back to the hotel. He simply wouldn't budge.

" Look, Shortie," he grumbled. " I know what I'm doing. And I've been away from the job long enough." But he did sit in the car most of the time.

" How soon will you be ready for the actual crossing? "
I asked.

" Probably tomorrow. The dredging's done and the sections are all tested."

" What's that thing they're welding on the end of that first joint? " I pointed to what the welder was doing.

" That's a heavy bull-plug with an eye to hitch the wire line that will pull the pipe."

While Dux was explaining, a man whom I recognized as the Detroit newspaper reporter stepped over to the car. He had done quite a write-up on the last fire.

" Hello," he greeted us, shaking hands with Dux. " Glad to see you out, Mr. Gentry. Sorry to hear about that accident."

" It could have been worse," Dux said, touching the bandage on his eye. " I'm O.K. now."

" Good. I'm here to cover the crossing," the reporter explained a little unnecessarily. " Mind telling me how you expect to go under the river? "

He took a notebook from his back pocket and a pencil from behind his ear. " I understand it'll be a sensational piece of engineering — this business of laying a pipeline without interrupting river traffic."

" Someone said it couldn't be done," I said proudly.

" From the way he handled that fire I covered and other things I've heard about," the young man said, smiling at me, " you have every right to be proud of him. Seems to me that husband of yours is quite a guy."

Dux squirmed. " About this river crossing," he said shortly. " If it weren't for the railroad tracks," he pointed toward the woods, " this job would be easy. We'd have room to weld up the entire three thousand feet and pull it across with a wire line, slacking it when a boat passed."

The reporter's pencil flew over the page. "That means you'll have to stop pulling after each six hundred feet in order to tie in the next section, eh?" he queried.

Dux nodded. "The trick is to keep the wire line in the ditch so that the boats can run over it without hurting their propellers or damaging our pipeline." He stopped, watching the reporter's pencil, and then went on, "To do this, we're going to put a snatch block on an anchor in the ditch under the dredge." He pointed to the men working on the Canadian side of the channel. "That's what they're doing now — running the wire line through the snatch block and bringing it to the American side to attach to the pipe."

"Snatch block," I repeated, without the faintest idea what it meant. I'm familiar with construction operations, but the terminology gets me down. Evidently the reporter knew what it was, for his pencil didn't stop for a second.

"Great," the reporter applauded, placing the pencil behind his ear. "This'll make a whale of a story. I sure want to be here; when will you do it?"

"Tomorrow — didn't you say, Dux?" I said helpfully.

Dux nodded, got out of the car, and walked toward the ditch.

"That's Sunday," the reporter said. "Judging by the crowds out here during the week, there'll be a mob tomorrow." He put his notebook in his back pocket and smiled at me. "'By, now. See you tomorrow."

Sunday morning dawned bright and clear, a beautiful fall day. We got out to the job by five thirty. For hours I watched the huge tractors with the heavy side booms lifting and carrying the pipe down the ditch into the river. Dux sat in one of our trucks, equipped with a two-way radio, and directed the men on the dredge where another of our radios had been installed. There was nothing about

232

his manner to indicate that he was doing anything out of the ordinary. But to say I was thrilled is a masterpiece in understatement. It was like watching a fabulous movie, with modern industry and human ingenuity playing the leading roles — and the man I loved in the director's seat!

By nine o'clock the crowds began to gather, and by eleven the state police came to keep the cars and people from blocking the highway. All day the operation went on: *push* from our side and *pull* from the dredge boat on the Canadian side.

Finally, around four o'clock, it was all over. Nothing to do now but wait for the action of the river to cover the ditch.

Tankers and ore boats were going up and down the river and I borrowed a pair of field glasses from the newspaper reporter to watch them pass. The crews stood out on deck, probably wondering what had drawn such crowds and why all the fanfare.

24

SOMEHOW, I LIKE to think of river crossings, with their changing methods, as symbolic of the progress of modern industry. In some ways, they're like people, each with a problem all its own. And, until human ingenuity stepped in, it was necessary to meet these problems, sometimes, with inadequate tools.

I feel too that the river crossings I remember so well from the earlier days were steppingstones for us, whatever the cost in obstacles. The more complicated they were, the greater the challenge, the more satisfying the accomplishment.

Not so long ago I was one of a group of women at a luncheon when the conversation turned to taxes and the high cost of living.

"Did you know the price of gasoline has gone up three cents? It's getting so it costs too much even to drive! I think if all of us would band together — you know, sort of go on a strike — "

"And now they're trying to increase the gas rates," a second woman broke in.

"Goodness knows, it's high enough already," another complained. "My bill last month for cooking alone was almost twelve dollars."

I looked at her. Three dollars a week — a little over forty

cents a day, I figured silently, remembering how Mrs. Dean and Mrs. May used to wrestle all winter with their old-fashioned ranges, sometimes chopping the wood that went into them. I remembered the smelly coal-oil stoves we used to fight during the summer — forever and a day scrubbing the sooty blackness off the bottoms of kettles.

But of course these women couldn't possibly know the cost in hardships, disappointments, heartaches — and, yes, money — to produce the finished products so that they might cook or heat their houses with ease and step on the starter to go where they liked, I thought. It's human nature, I guess, to take our modern way of life for granted, though a lot depends on where you sit, what you've seen, what you've lived through.

Driving home, I thought of the time Dux was burned in the gas fire, the trouble he'd had in eastern Kentucky, the dangerous fires he had fought, the hours he'd worked overtime at the rigs or the office and then come home to study. I thought of the enormous investments thrown into dry holes, lease rentals, and pipelines, and the part they had played in making America and its homes what they are today — places in which comfort and convenience are accepted as a matter of course.

I thought of other men, like Dux, in other fields, who must have followed a similar pattern. I thought of their wives too, and wondered if they'd been as happy, as bone-tired — and as crazily daring as I'd been.

I thought of the many flower seeds I'd planted only to move before they bloomed; of the cabins, shacks, and furnished rooms Dux and I had lived in before he fixed up the tents, and how the high light of a routine existence was an occasional business trip into the city.

How often had I left dirty dishes in the sink, beds unmade, to go with Dux, closing the door without a qualm!

For years I kept a suitcase under the bed, packed with our best clothes, so when Dux said, "Let's go," we went. Many's the time I've popped the kids into the car, grabbed a wet washcloth, and washed and dressed them while Dux drove. Life to me was where Dux was.

Oh, I'll admit there were times when I'd envy the life of a farmer's wife with her chickens, her garden, her chance to stay put; or the preacher's wife with her Tuesday guild or Friday circle that nothing was allowed to interrupt. But, looking back, I'd do it all over again. And so would our children. How often have I heard it said that moving around, changing schools, would ruin the children's education, destroy their sense of security? It hasn't had that effect on ours. No, their education improved with travel; they have gained poise, they are completely independent, and, as a family, we couldn't be any closer, even though they're married now with families of their own.

Dux and I still do crazy things together. Only last week I was putting the finishing touches to what I hoped would be an outstanding flower arrangement for the garden club that afternoon when the telephone rang and I heard Dux's voice.

"I've got to go to New York, Shortie," he said. "Can you make the eleven ten?"

I glanced at the hall clock. It was ten thirty. "Sure," I told him, glad that he wanted me to go with him. "I'll pack our bag and meet you at the train." Leaving the telephone, I flew into action, the garden club forgotten.

As I hurried into the station, Dux came toward me, a smile on his face. He took my arm and said in a singsong voice:

"'She caught the train she said she would,
And changed at junctions as she should . . .'"

236

Astonished, I looked at him. " Why, Dux Gentry, I haven't thought of that little old rhyme since we were first married! " Then I finished it:

" ' She left no little thing behind
    Excepting loving thoughts and kind.'

" At least — I hope," I added, and squeezed his arm.